Into the Arms of the
ANGELS

Into the Arms of the ANGELS

TRUE END-OF-LIFE STORIES

Candy Kinser RN BSN

Into the Arms of the Angels: True End-of-Life Stories

Praise for
Into the Arms of the Angels

"Candy Kinser captures the essence of care from the heart. Every individual patient story brings to light the importance of the work that hospice professionals perform on a daily basis. Acceptance, dignity, forgiveness, and love are the lines of poetry in each of our lives.

"Thank you, Candy, for reminding us that our lives matter to more people than we will ever know."

Chad Higbee
Former President, Oklahoma Hospice Association

"Anyone who has cared for dying persons and their families as either a professional or other caregiver should read *Into the Arms of the Angels: True End-of-Life Stories.* Candy Kinser uses her extensive hospice experience and eloquently and compassionately tells the story of many of her past patients and families. Her message is an important one – of hope, reassurance, and comfort."

Patricia Berry, PhD, RN, ACHPN, FPCN, FAAN
University of Utah College of Nursing

"Hospice patients represent one of the most vulnerable groups of patients. With this book Candy demonstrates how dignity is brought into the lives of these patients by caring nurses and other hospice providers."

Chad Kimball, M.D.

"Loved this book! The dying process can be a spirit-filled and peaceful time, as this book teaches. It was so with my parents, and I hope for the same! A *must* read!"

Janice Kapp Perry
Composer, Author, Lecturer

"Having worked with Candy Kinser for many years in our hospice service to hundreds of patients, including my own wife, I can honestly say that she is one of the most caring and compassionate individuals I have ever met. She is an outstanding hospice nurse, and I endorse her compassionate nursing service to others with all my heart."

Dr. John Garrett
Hospice Chaplain

"A comforting piece of literature about life after caregiving. True stories that conquer the fear of dying and instill faith in life after life. With multiple inspiring tales, author Candy Kinser brings hope and happiness to our hearts through her endearing tales."

Margarete de Gaston
LifeAfterCaregiving.com

"Assurance, confidence, and comfort in the most difficult time you will ever encounter. How can we deal with death and dying? Is there any positive message or support when we are told that our own condition, or that of our closest loved one, is terminal?

"In language we all can understand, Candy Kinser illuminates the process that carries one from this life into the next. Her knowledge and experience in hospice care open the soul to hope and joy . . . even in times like these."

Reverend Robert E. Helsel

To seekers of truth—may you appreciate the inherent wisdom of your body.

I am honored to be your friend.

To each member of my family—your goodness has given me the opportunity to serve our community.

I cherish you.

To those who protect the two great bonding moments in life—birth and death.

I treasure my association with you.

I am proud to be one of you.

Table of Contents

Introduction

Every aspect of my life has been enriched because of my association with the dying. I am amazed at the wealth of experience I have encountered while stumbling about in my career. Where I have been clumsy, an unseen force has guided my steps so that I might share a fundamental truth: our bodies know how to die.

We do not need to fear death.

Through the pages of this book, we will travel a journey of discovery. Facts hidden in the halls of medicine will come into focus. The truth can set us free from the anxiety of dying.

In his landmark book *Tuesdays With Morrie*, Mitch Albom shares Morrie's wise comment, "Once you learn how to die, you learn how to live."

Dying patients—and their families—have taught me much that I could learn in no other way. Their stories are rich with inspiration.

Come join me in their homes. Sit by their bedside. Hear their whispered words. Learn of the miracles shared by patients who are about to enter into eternity.

It has been said that when the student is ready, the teacher presents. Our teachers are the wisest, the best . . . our teachers are angels.

- Candy Kinser

Confessions of a Hospice Nurse

I never wanted to work with patients who were dying. When I finished nursing school, I went to work in a large children's hospital. However, after a year I had an intense desire to move into intensive care. Soon I found myself in a large critical care unit. It was fun and exciting to be part of that tight team of nurses. We recovered all the heart surgery patients right on the unit. Many lives were saved there.

However, once again, I eventually found myself searching for something different. Looking back, I realize that I became dissatisfied because of a variety of situations that I experienced in the ICU.

I wish I could take you there.

When a code blue was announced, we ran! We grabbed the crash cart and ran! So did someone from the respiratory therapy team, and someone from the pharmacy, and someone from the group of residents. We converged on the patient and quickly ushered the family out of the room. The code began by stripping the patient and shocking them. John always loved to do the shocking, so we would hand him the defibrillator. When we administered chest compressions, we could sometimes feel the ribs crack in our elderly patients. As the doctor intubated the patient, we listened to the chest. If the tube was misplaced, air would flow into the stomach instead of the lungs, and we would try again. Finally the patient was hooked up to a ventilator. Then we would draw arterial blood gases so that we would know how to tweak the ventilator. The needle was inserted into a wrist at 90 degrees. It hurt!

After the code, we bid our friends from respiratory therapy and the pharmacy goodbye until the next time.

Don't get me wrong. I'm not against codes. But I *am* against their indiscriminate use. There is a time to be born and a time to die. If it is obvious that it is my time to die, please don't attempt to resuscitate me.

For example, we had a frail, elderly, terminally ill patient admitted to our unit. During shift change, I asked, "Has anyone spoken to the family about initiating a 'Do Not Resuscitate' (DNR) order?"

"Why would you want to do that?" responded our unit supervisor.

A friend pulled me aside immediately after the meeting and counseled me to "never mention DNR again, or you could be fired."

I didn't. But I did think about it . . . a lot.

I thought about it when we were caring for the grandmother of a sweet family. After putting her through such a code, the family decided they didn't want us to ever do that again. So we didn't. She died shortly thereafter, and I informed the family as they surrounded her bed. They stood there, watching her chest rising and falling, and one of them said, "But she's still breathing."

I explained, "No, that's just the ventilator pushing in air. See this flat line on the monitor? That means her heart isn't beating anymore. The doctor hasn't arrived yet to pronounce the death, so I can't turn off the ventilator. He'll be here shortly."

They continued to stand there watching her chest rise and fall as if the whole thing didn't make sense. Perhaps they wanted to hug her, say goodbye, and cry. But there was so much in the way: a tube-feeding pump, multiple IV lines, a noisy respirator, side rails, and the unnatural imposition of the entire setting.

I believe that birth and death are two times when nature does all it can to force us to push aside the world and concentrate on each other as intimate participants in grand moments of bonding and love.

All too often, an insensitive medical system interferes with such precious and fleeting moments.

I was part of that system.

One day as I stood by the bedside suctioning a woman, who was ventilator dependent, the word "hospice" just entered my mind. It was shift change. Kathy, another nurse and my friend, entered the room. I asked, "Kathy, what do you think of hospice?"

Kathy responded, "Well, considering that that's what I have always wanted to do, if I ever got a chance to work in hospice, I'd jump at it."

The next day I was making calls to some local hospices, and was given the opportunity to follow Gracie for a day. She had been a nurse for thirty-two years, and a hospice nurse for four. I was impressed with the quality of comfort and peace in the lives of her patients. It was obvious that they looked forward to her visits. I was becoming hooked on hospice.

chapter

Hooked on Hospice

My first hospice death involved an elderly doctor in a nursing home. When I entered his room at the far end of a quiet hall, I immediately recognized that he was actively dying. I went to the nurse's station to call his daughter. Then I quickly returned to his side.

How peaceful the setting!

He was in a coma. Breathing was labored with periods of apnea (no breathing) coming regularly every minute. I watched his every breath. This was a different kind of death than anything I had experienced previously in the ICU. I wanted to learn everything possible from this dying physician.

His daughter and her husband arrived in about an hour. Instantly, as they entered the room, prior to their speaking or even approaching the bed, his facial expression changed. I knew that he knew that they were there. Somehow he knew. With her husband standing at her side, and without hesitation, the old physician's daughter leaned close, held onto his hand, and said, "Daddy, I love you so much!"

She told him many more precious things—the things that matter most. Nothing separated them. No intimidating IV lines, tube feedings, ventilators, or suction machines. No noisy monitors. No side rails. No rules and restrictions about visitors. And most importantly, no code teams rushing in and throwing them out.

Several times when he lay breathless, the apnea extensive, her eyes would search for mine, silently asking if that was it, if all was over. Without words, I assured her that he was still there. Gradually, as the apnea lengthened to forty-plus seconds, and his breathing rate slowed to only six breaths per minute, we knew he was slipping away.

And then it happened, a last peaceful breath.

She cried. Her husband cried. He held her tight. But the sobs were swallowed up in bonds of raw resounding love, strengthening between them. And I knew that I was witnessing a final gift given to this daughter by a tender father.

That scene will live forever in my mind.

I practically ran back to the hospice office. "Gracie, Gracie, I did it! I pulled in the family, and they were able to say goodbye. It was so perfectly special. But Gracie, I don't understand. This death was so different. His breathing never became agonal, and I never had to suction him."

She looked at my younger inexperienced face and said with a smile, "Candy, that's what hospice is all about."

It was official. I was hopelessly hooked on hospice.

We were having guests for dinner that night. I arrived late, but jubilant. They politely asked how my day at work had been. I said, "Great! A man died, and it was so fabulous!"

A look of disbelief appeared on their faces. Perhaps they were having second thoughts about my dinner. However, a tempting meal lured them to the table. Now I had a captive audience, and I shared why I was so excited.

You see, I had just learned that our bodies know how to die. Just as our bodies know what to do when it's time to give birth, our bodies know what to do when it's time to let go. Generally, the release comes peacefully, with nature providing the orchestration.

When I was a little girl, the prospect of death terrified me. I would lie in bed at night and try to imagine what it must be like to die. I knew that when people die, they don't breathe. So I held my breath to simulate death. Soon I was forced to gasp for air. I just knew that to die must be a most horrifying experience.

As patients approach their "time to die," they seem to need a more inward focus and spiritual energy. They exhibit diminished interest in superficial activities. They may seem withdrawn, which indicates a "letting go."

For example, a patient who previously enjoyed television and the newspaper may now lie on the bed, content to simply rest in quiet surroundings. Lethargy is common and increases as the days and weeks pass. Naps may become frequent and increase in length. Food may lose much of its appeal. Eating becomes an intrusion. Digestion is hard work. The body does not consider it a priority at this time.

As we prepare to die, our bodies begin to close down our physiological functions, cascading gradually, one system following another, until ultimately the need for oxygen no longer exists.

Hallelujah! There need be no terrible lingering in an agonal phase while one struggles for every breath.

While working in intensive care, I didn't have the luxury of allowing this gradual closure of body systems. I fought death valiantly along side my team of fellow soldiers. If a patient didn't feel like eating, no problem; we'd push a tube down their nose, hook them up to a pump, and force tube feedings. If a patient didn't feel like drinking, no problem; we'd insert an intravenous line and push fluids. This was a huge obstacle for patients who were actually approaching their "time to die." A frail, elderly body trying to achieve closure couldn't deal with all this extra liquid. Their lungs would begin to fill, and breathing became a struggle. Alarms would sound, and we'd rush into the room to suction the patient and save them from drowning. We looked important to those who watched us come to the victim's rescue.

However, these heroic-looking actions were futile. How can a body prepare to die if it isn't allowed to do what it inherently and instinctively knows how to do? How can a body die if it keeps receiving mixed signals that interfere with the natural processes trying to occur?

Dr. Joseph V. Simone, clinical director emeritus of the Huntsman Cancer Institute and professor emeritus of pediatrics and medicine at the University of Utah, recently stated in an article published in Oncology Times, February 2004, "It is a shame that we oncologists fail to use hospices sooner in the course of management, and too often, at the cost of proper palliative care, employ futile anti-cancer therapy. The latter often holds out false hope instead of providing more appropriate end-of-life care. Why is it done? It is not easy to tell a patient and family that there is no effective cancer therapy left; and, sad to say, too often economics plays a role. Offering hospice and other end-of-life care is not abandonment or 'having no therapy to offer,' but is a different specific kind of therapy—a therapy that for many patients is more appropriate and more humane."

Leann Jackson, a dear friend and an amazing hospice nurse, shares the thoughts she wrote while sitting at a patient's bedside:

The Homecoming

The labored breath escapes his body. I watch him and I wait, mostly due to force of habit, for the next shallow breath. I wait . . . and I find myself reflecting on what this sweet man's life must have been like.

At one time he was vibrant, young, and ready to take on the world. He threw rocks, picked up bugs, put a worm on a hook, rode a bike, and marveled at how amazing it was that God could make a fuzzy caterpillar into a beautiful butterfly.

He received an education, played basketball, caught a pass, hit one out, teased the girls, goofed off with his friends, and fell in love.

He married his sweetheart, marveled at the birth of his son, began a career, went to Church, and honored God.

He got up most mornings, bright and early, showered and shaved his handsome face, got dressed the same way every day, and went off to support those who loved and trusted him.

Perhaps he liked to sing.

Perhaps he could really move on the dance floor.

Perhaps he secretly loved birthdays and Valentine's Day.

Perhaps he cried when he lost a pet, a friend, his parents, and the love of his life.

He got old. It was hard to walk, unassisted. Hard to eat, unassisted. Hard to live, unassisted.

What an amazing and interesting circle life is!

I wait . . . and the only sounds I hear are the ticking of the clock on the stark, white wall above his head . . . young, vibrant people competing in a contest on TV in the next room . . . traffic rushing somewhere on the freeway outside the window.

Not a sound from the man lying in the bed next to my chair.

Except to an honored few, his life has gone relatively unnoticed by the world . . . as well as his passing. Quietly, unassuming, and disturbing no one, he slips into his new world.

I sit alone . . . but surrounded by angels, and feel so grateful to have been invited to his homecoming.

Leann Jackson

(Used by permission)

I am in good company. Obviously others are also hooked on hospice.

In the hospice setting, I offer fluid and food as the patient desires, but I don't force them upon an unwilling patient. Hospice patients eventually refuse almost all sustenance. When I arrive at a home and am informed that the patient isn't even drinking anymore, I know that my patient may now be entering the "actively dying" phase. This occurs during the last week of life. In this phase they don't usually experience hunger or thirst as we do. In fact, they may clamp their lips shut if you attempt to feed them.

What most people don't understand is that the natural dehydration that occurs with this phase actually adds to their comfort. It causes natural endorphins to be released. It facilitates easier breathing. I've observed congestive heart failure patients who gradually lose all edema (excess fluid) and breathe easier than they had previously.

Although this patient is weak, it still isn't quite time for them to leave this existence. The body compensates, even while closing down systems, so they can live a few more days. All vital signs rise. While others are probably breathing about twelve to sixteen times a minute, they may be breathing around forty-four times per minute. Their heart is beating faster, and their blood pressure and temperature are also elevated. The body is working. Just as with birth, there is a labor to be performed. Labor can be emotionally and physically draining. If a family is falsely informed that the patient will die today or tomorrow, and their actual death doesn't occur for six to seven days, the labor will seem even more draining, and the family may be emotionally exhausted.

But the labor of dying is a precious time when family gather 'round the bedside. It's amazing to watch how the act of dying facilitates a uniting process between family and friends. Bonds of love are strengthened as siblings and parents discuss old memories and pull out photograph albums. This is a good time to speak of gifts. Gifts can be given to the departing loved one.

Dying patients are cool. They know what really matters. I recently heard a marvelous phrase, "We may not have it all together, but together we have it all." If a dying patient is in the peaceful presence of loved ones, they have it all. What else matters? They relish the sound of loved one's voices. Touch is everything. If you hold their hand or touch their forehead, you have just given them more than a million dollars.

You are a gift. Just your presence provides comfort. They may be too weak to speak or even open their eyes, but their sense of hearing is very sensitive.

At some point, the body tires of compensating, and the vital signs begin to fall. I call this "getting over the hump" or "getting through transition." From then on, the process accelerates. Be sure that any who need to come are notified. Now the breathing rate begins to slow. You'll know. Labored breathing is often a bit noisy. This is a blessing. You can putter about the house, doing those necessary things like eating and going to the bathroom. But when that breathing rate changes, you will immediately be drawn to the bedside—almost instinctively. Respiratory changes are significant. The heart will begin to slow, and the blood pressure will nicely and gradually decline.

I didn't let that happen in the ICU. There I would hang an IV bag of dobutamine and force the blood pressure back up. But not here. Here is hospice. Here we get to throw away cookbook medicine and practice common sense. The top number of a blood pressure reading represents the systolic pressure. This is the amount of pressure in the arterial system when the heart is contracting. The bottom number represents the diastolic pressure. This is the amount of pressure in the arterial system when the heart is relaxing. I've found that when there is only a very small difference between the systolic and diastolic pressure, then the body is rapidly approaching expiration.

Don't be surprised if, at some point, the patient reports seeing a deceased loved one or being of light. It is a common phenomenon. I have many such stories to share.

How can a patient live so long without drinking? Ahh . . . that's the beauty of our bodies. They become so amazingly efficient. The body may become perfectly still, not moving in any perceptible way. Even the act of breathing may cease for several moments, periodically allowing the body to completely rest. Then, after a pause of ten to thirty seconds, breathing resumes.

Circulation slows to areas where it is no longer essential. You may observe mottling (blood pooling on the underside of the body) as you help turn the patient. Feet and hands may be cool to the touch. The extremities have long since ceased to move. The lower extremities let go of their strength first. Who needs legs when one is actively dying? Arm strength lingers a bit longer. Arms are important for hugs. And hugs are important when one is leaving for a supremely ultimate adventure. So also are the brain, heart, and lungs. Oxygen continues to be directed there until all work on earth is finished.

At this point, you stand or sit close to the bed. The character of respirations may change significantly and/or slow. These changes are quite noticeable. Still your presence is a comfort. In the morning, our patient may be breathing at a rate of only twelve times per minute. Sometimes the breaths are so shallow they are barely discernible. By mid-afternoon, the rate of breathing may be down to ten times per minute with periods of apnea stretching to fifteen or twenty seconds. Then, as evening approaches and the room is quiet, we may be seeing longer periods of apnea and only eight or nine breaths per minute. A half-hour can pass, and breaths fall to a rate of only six or seven. Apnea is lasting so long, almost a minute. Everyone gathers close. No one speaks. A final breath—and all is still.

An experience has transpired between those present that will forever connect them to one another. As a hospice provider, I am satisfied. I know that together our team has once again protected a time that will be forever cherished.

As I wrote this chapter, my own mother lay in a distant city, close to her "time to die."

"Candy, I don't want to go on," she whispered over the phone.

Would a hospice nurse be there, at the right place and the right time for her and for me?

I prayed that would be the case, for to have a hand in the great work of hospice is to give a most cherished gift and to share life to the fullest.

chapter

Blaine

It is with great respect that I write the story of Blaine. I remember well the first day we met.

As I approached the nursing home, I searched for a parking spot under a tree. The nursing facility sat on a corner in an old residential neighborhood, and visitors parked along the street. I knew I'd rather walk a few more steps than return to a hot car. The water bottle that I had grabbed, as I was leaving home, was there in my car. By eleven o'clock, the water would be too hot to drink.

I parked opposite the facility. Before opening the car door, my eyes searched the front passenger seat for everything I would need: my nursing bag, notebook, a blank form, and a pen. One must have a pen! Just try and find an unclaimed pen in a nursing home!

I grabbed my things, scurried out of the car, walked across the street, and entered the facility. It was not a place to which patients come by choice. Each patient had a story; perhaps they broke a hip, perhaps they had a stroke. But for each, something had happened that forced them into this place.

There were some smiles here. But they were not the uninhibited smiles of great happiness. Even genuine smiles revealed an element of sadness, of grief for what once was.

Except for Blaine's smile.

I cautiously peered at Blaine from his doorway.

You never quite know what to expect when first meeting a patient. Patients are not superficial. They are what they are. There are those who, by nature, are polite, kind, and appreciative. There are those who are not. Some appear sane initially, but soon reveal another side. I've been cursed at, spit upon, threatened, and even hit. Some patients are simply overwhelmed.

Blaine looked at me with a huge smile of great peace and profound joy. A light in the darkness! I instinctively dropped the appropriate formal introduction and called him by his first name. Thus began our instant friendship and bond of respect.

I looked forward to each visit. His joy was infectious and constant—even with bedsores. Blaine had a line of bedsores extending up his spine. He expected them to heal. I didn't. However, upon inspection a few weeks later, I found every sore almost completely gone. I had never seen such a miraculously quick healing.

He baffled the doctors. Once, in our weekly team meeting, I overheard the astonished medical director ask why, given his poor physical condition, Blaine Gardner was still alive. Blaine's previous nurse spoke up and responded, "I don't know . . . the man talks to God!"

Blaine's children spoke of a father who always cared. They said he was honest and tried to do the right things. I wasn't surprised. I knew he valued holy writ. It was not uncommon for him to mention a specific passage of scripture during our visits. He was one of the most spiritually uninhibited patients I had ever known.

It was a busy day when the call came.

"Candy, Blaine's dying! Come as fast as you can! He's bluer than the sky!"

I dropped everything. Soon I was at Blaine's bedside. One thin worn sheet covered his body.

But Blaine didn't die. Once again he defied all expectations.

Several days later, as Blaine recovered, he was anxious to tell me what actually happened.

"Candy, my wife was here."

Blaine's wife had died several years earlier in that very nursing home, in that very room. "She stood right there, in front of the closet, and held out her arms. 'Blaine, won't you join me?' she asked. I had to tell her that I haven't yet finished my work on the earth. She was so beautiful! She looked like she was about twenty-three years old, and her hair was long again, down to her shoulders."

I didn't think it was possible, but my ever-happy friend was even happier! This man, whose whole persona was one of joy, was now experiencing an even greater joy, a joy beyond anything earthly. For him, it was more than faith; he knew, he knew what was just around the corner – and he was totally and completely delighted.

In the following weeks, Blaine's smile of peace never waned. Most people would find his circumstance dismal, yet he continued to be elated—and he was especially elated about his impending death!

Blaine's son moved away and had Blaine transferred to his new home, out of my area. I thought of Blaine often. Hospice nurses hold their patients in their hearts forever.

Incredibly, Blaine lived another year. When I was informed that he had died, it was easy to picture him walking into the arms of a very loving wife. I envision her as beautiful beyond description, young, and with hair flowing.

Death is the beginning of a life joyous beyond description.

I believe Blaine wanted us to know.

Eunice

As I said before, dying patients are actually very cool people. They often teach those waiting by their side illuminating truths. Such was Eunice.

Eunice grew up in Brazil, but she had been living in the United States for many years. She, and her husband of forty years, lived in a clean, bright, humble townhouse. She was only fifty-nine years old. She was dying of metastatic breast cancer.

Prior to our first visit, I looked over my assignment sheet and observed Eunice's birth date. Oh no! When I saw her birth year, I knew that my visits with her would have a greater than normal element of stress.

No one plans on dying in their fifties. Such patients grieve over stolen time, over life cut short. They feel that this is not supposed to happen!

In these cases, my arrival represents premature death—a very unwelcome reality! As uncomfortable as it is to be in this position, experienced hospice teams know that there is a far greater concern: how to make a difference in the face of such sorrowful distress?

And so, as I grabbed my bag and left the car to enter Eunice's home, I said a silent prayer. "Help me, please help me . . . and let them know I care."

Eunice was sitting on the couch. There were several small pillows carefully placed to beautify the living room. One of her two daughters was there with her.

"Hi, I'm Candy, one of the nurses from hospice."

"I'm Rosa, and this is my mother, Eunice."

I responded, "Eunice, I understand that you have been going through some tough times."

"Oh yes, but Rosa and Maria, my girls, have been taking good care of me."

Eunice's husband, Ricardo, relied heavily on their two daughters. And the girls adored their mother. One, or both of them, was usually present when I visited.

Soon I was sitting by Eunice's side, checking her vital signs and asking routine questions about pain and other issues related to comfort.

But not every visit was so routine. Late one Tuesday afternoon the office called to report that Maria, Eunice's daughter, was very upset. I immediately called their home. Maria answered the phone as if it were a lifeline.

"Maria, what is happening?"

"Oh Candy, I don't know what is happening! Mom was sitting on the couch just now, and she picked up a pillow and attempted to eat it! What is going on?"

I swallowed hard. There were no easy answers. "It could be several things. The cancer may have advanced into the brain, and medications could be impacting your mother cognitively. The time of day may even play a part. Symptoms often worsen as the sun begins to go down. The term 'sundowners' reflects this phenomenon."

"What can we do? I hate seeing Mom this way. This will upset Dad."

"I'm on my way."

Ricardo and the girls were having a tough time observing Eunice's decline. I quickly learned that the best response to each of Eunice's emergencies was to simply assure them, "I'm on my way."

Most hospice patients are quite thin, or emaciated, as we tend to say. This loss of body mass actually makes the process of dying easier. But Eunice had a significant amount of extra weight and fluid. Therefore, I expected her final days to be more challenging.

I spent a lot of time at their home during the last two weeks of Eunice's life. With her advanced cancer, it became necessary to diligently monitor her comfort. The discolored tumors were protruding through the skin of her upper arms. It was very difficult for Rosa and Maria to watch their once-vibrant mom require continual assistance.

It was even more difficult for Ricardo. Good men want to "fix" things for those they love. When they can't, when it's out of their control, it can be very frustrating for them. Sometimes men leave the room, not because they don't care, but because of frustration. They may feel like a failure.

On one such frustrating day, Ricardo had walked out of the room. Eunice was in a coma. We nurses had begun a schedule of hospice care called continuous care, in which we take turns staying for extended periods of time. This was a scary time for them. They were losing the heart and center of their home. Eunice had been an amazing wife and mother. She loved her family unconditionally.

As she lay unconscious in her upstairs bedroom, we gathered around the bed and talked about the past. I remembered how much I previously enjoyed listening to Eunice. Although raised in Brazil, she always spoke fluent English. She even served as a translator.

After a while, I got up, wrote an entry into a chart, and returned to sit on the side of Eunice's bed. We were feeling very informal and very close—the closer the better. Rosa was standing next to the bed, on the opposite side, staring at her mother.

Then something amazing happened. I had never seen anything quite like it before. Actively dying patients don't abruptly awake from a coma and articulately speak loud and clear.

But suddenly Eunice's eyes opened wider than I have ever seen anyone's eyes open . . . and she spoke! But she didn't speak in English. She spoke in her native Portuguese. I didn't understand what she said, but I'll never forget the excited intonation in her voice. And she said the exact same thing, the exact same way—twice!

Rosa looked at me and translated, "She just said, 'It is so pretty! It is so pretty!'" Then Rosa added, "I asked Mom to come back and tell us what the other side is like." Rosa continued to stare at me, trying to take in the reality of what had just happened. Then she looked back at her mother while reaching for her mother's hand.

Rosa believed in life after death. She had hoped that her mother would somehow be able to return after dying and tell her about eternity. Rosa was surprised. She didn't expect the answer to come like this, yet she immediately recognized it as the answer she was seeking.

As death approaches, the separation between dimensions becomes thin. It is as if patients are lovingly prepared and tutored for this grand journey we call death. Accordingly, the natural dying process includes a time of inward focus. Patients are content to lie peacefully, often sleeping for extended periods. When they awaken, even if for but a moment, they sometimes share precious mysteries, often involving previously departed loved ones.

Ricardo needed to know what had just happened. I stood up and went looking for him. I found him in the next room, kneeling in prayer. If he knew I was there, he didn't indicate any such awareness. He continued his silent prayer. Unusually bold, I walked over to his sacred place and rested my hand on his shoulder.

"Ricardo, Eunice just spoke. She opened her eyes and declared, 'It is so pretty!' She said it twice."

The ever-quiet Ricardo didn't say anything to me. He rose to his feet and purposefully walked into Eunice's room and to her side. Bending down and putting his mouth next to her ear (remember, we nurses were charting that she was in a coma), he yelled, "Eunice, who are you with, Eunice?"

Much to everyone's surprise, she spoke again. Just one word; the last she ever said. But, oh, what a window of vision she gave us with her answer! She spoke a Portuguese name.

Rosa, still holding her mother's hand, looked directly at me and explained. Eunice had said a name. Rosa's eyes widened as she realized the significance of her Mother's response, even while explaining, "That was mother's best friend . . . in Brazil . . . and . . . *she* died two years ago!"

It was as though we were standing on holy ground. We will never forget a mother's answer to her daughter's petition: Please come back and tell us what the other side is like.

Eunice has spoken, "It is so pretty!"

chapter 5

Sarah

As I pulled onto their street, I began to drive very slowly, my eyes searching for the right address. I was looking for the home of Sarah and Joe. As I came upon their tiny house, I realized there was nothing unusual about their home. All the homes in this section of town were small. In fact, the humble commonness of their home hid any evidence of the great struggle happening inside. Did any of the neighbors know?

Sarah and Joe, who were in their sixties, had married right out of high school. They were wonderful grandparents. Sarah loved to sew for her grandchildren.

Joe showed me a small sewing room where he had built shelves to hold the bolts of fabric Sarah purchased. Sarah would carefully place each selected piece of fabric on a shelf, in loving anticipation. That way, even as she sewed, she could envision the prospective gifts that she would soon give to a delighted child.

My eyes searched the shelves. I could tell from Sarah's selections that she and Joe had grandsons and granddaughters. There were robust blues and pastel pinks; a jar of buttons and yards and yards of lace.

But Sarah's grandchildren would never again know the joy of dressing in a new garment sewn with Grandma's love.

Grandma was dying.

Six weeks earlier, as Sarah sat down to finish pinning a pattern on two yards of denim, she felt too weak to push the pins. Joe was concerned. He knew she had lost some weight recently, but this was not like Sarah. She was always full of energy, especially when beginning a new project. She said she would be fine, "I just need some extra rest."

Early the next morning Sarah slipped out of bed and went into the kitchen. Joe lay in the bed hoping that all would be fine. But within a few minutes, he heard a groan. He hurried out of bed and found Sarah bending forward while leaning on the table, obviously in pain.

"That's it, you are going to the doctor," he declared. Sarah began to cry. She didn't want to know. Their humble life was perfect as it was; she could sew and be close to Joe. If this bit of heaven was about to change, she didn't want to know.

Lab tests were completed, but they came back normal. The doctor arranged for Sarah to have a CT scan and finally a biopsy.

Joe and Sarah returned home with something new. Not a piece of fabric, but something that would forever change the fabric of their lives—a diagnosis of pancreatic cancer.

The diagnosis was ever present with them. It was at the dinner table that night. They spoke very little. Both Joe and Sarah felt overwhelmed. They were in that phase called "denial."

Joe hoped that if they didn't talk about it, if they didn't let anything change, they could hold on to their life together—a bit longer. Living without Sarah was unthinkable. Not talking about it was his way of banishing the blasted diagnosis.

Sarah hoped that the doctor was wrong. She always recovered in the past. "Spring will soon be here, and I'll feel better . . . maybe."

But the diagnosis refused to be ignored. Joe was amazed at how quickly Sarah declined. She ate very little because of nausea. She felt tired and weak. She was too weak to finish the last few seams of a dress she had already cut out for their granddaughter.

And there was pain. Joe hated to see her in pain. The doctor had suggested hospice, but Sarah didn't want strangers coming into their home. I believe it was the pain that finally caused Joe to make a call requesting our help.

And so I came. I immediately fell in love with this sweet couple. My first priority was to help eliminate Sarah's pain. That part was easy. But what about Joe's pain? As a hospice team we joined together to support Joe.

There was nothing we could do to keep Sarah from leaving him. But Joe knew we cared. And that seemed to lift his spirit. We brought Joe pies. How he missed Sarah's homemade pies. But I think the thing he missed most was Sarah moving about in their kitchen, creating delicious treats, making their little home a heaven.

He liked to see us go to Sarah, hold her hand, kiss her head, and massage her feet . . . anything. Anything we did to comfort Sarah was a comfort to Joe. We spoke her name with love. That was easy to do. We loved her. We learned that the best way to ease Joe's pain, was to ease Sarah's pain.

It was a privilege to come into their home. I felt so grateful for the hospice program that brought us together. In a busy, isolated, money-motivated world, hospice opens doors and invites us into the hearts of beautiful people.

Finally, one day I arrived to say goodbye to Sarah. During the previous week, Sarah had entered the active dying phase. We had been coming every day.

This was an especially hard time for Joe. He was powerless to fix this. He could fix Sarah's stove and her sewing machine—but he couldn't fix this. And this was not an easy death. Sarah kept hanging on. But why?

When I told Joe that I knew it was hard for him to see Sarah linger, he confided in me. He told me that they had a son who had not yet come to say goodbye to his mother. Joe sobbed, "But he's on his way. He's coming in from Kentucky, and he will be here in a few hours."

I understood. I had experienced this before. If a patient senses that there is unfinished business—perhaps a loved one hasn't yet arrived—or there is unresolved conflict, the patient may linger beyond what is normal. This often facilitates a needed happening.

Why? I don't know. I have decided that perhaps heaven respects the feelings of the patient. Anyway, this phenomenon is common to experienced hospice workers, be they nurses, aides, chaplains, social workers, doctors, or volunteers.

I walked into the tiny living room where Sarah lay on a hospital bed. I felt I was on holy ground. I knelt down by Sarah's side and asked if she was in pain. She said, "No." Amazingly, even after actively dying for almost a week, she was coherent, and her answers—although very weak—were clear and appropriate. I went into the bathroom, ran cool water over a worn washcloth, and returned to place it on Sarah's pale forehead.

I took a seat by her side. I knew Joe didn't want her to be alone, and I felt that my presence might comfort Sarah. Joe was in the kitchen. She and I were alone.

After some time had passed, Sarah opened her eyes, looked up towards the corner of the ceiling and said, "No, you can't." There was a pause while Sarah seemed to be listening. And then, still looking up, she spoke, saying, "Let me see it then." Those were her exact words. They were the last words I ever heard Sarah speak.

Johnny, Sarah's son, arrived from Kentucky that afternoon. He came to tell his mother that he loved her. Their reunion was a very personal and private time. Sarah couldn't, wouldn't leave until Johnny came. Even in dying, she gave her son this gift. She died shortly after Johnny's arrival.

And what about the words I heard her speak? I can only surmise what must have been happening. I believe someone referred to as an "angel," perhaps a previously departed family member, came to take Sarah home. Perhaps that was why she was looking so intently at the corner of the ceiling. Perhaps the angel said, "I'm here to take you home." To which Sarah responded, "No you can't." I suppose the angel then said something like, "But it is so beautiful here." To which she responded, "Let me see it then."

I'll never know exactly what was said to Sarah. But I'll never forget her words as I observed one side of that undeniable conversation.

chapter

Rebecca

The caregivers who provide long term and intimate care of the dying are not atheists. How can one remain atheistic when one's daily walk is with patients poised at the edge of eternity? Their stories, although simple and personal, ring with a consistent clarity of pitch that is unmistakable to the experienced.

Such was the ring of Rebecca's story. It opened the ears of her caregivers, even as it opened Rebecca's eyes and voice.

Rebecca lived in a long-term care nursing facility in the northwest corner of the city. She had lived there for many years. Her caregivers had become familiar with her depressed state. Rebecca was blind, demented, and depressed. She sat every day slumped over in her wheelchair. She didn't raise her head. She didn't smile. She didn't talk. She hadn't responded positively in years.

Every week I made the pilgrimage to check on Rebecca and to make sure that her needs were being met. Things were always the same.

However, one time, shortly before her death, things were not the same. The facility nurses and several aides were happy and excited to report about Rebecca. Their conversation went pretty much like this:

"Candy, Rebecca smiled and talked to us!"

"What? You can't be talking about my Rebecca."

"Yes, we are! Rebecca smiled and said that she saw Michael! You know she's blind! We called her daughter. Her daughter told us that she had a brother who died in infancy. His name was Michael! What do you think about that?"

I didn't have to think very long to realize the significance of what they had just shared. Rebecca's story, like so many others, rang of truth—indisputable truth—consistent with the common miracles that surround the dying.

Rebecca was able to see, and so can we!

chapter 7

Utana

To understand the story of Utana, one must first understand her nurse. The nurse who cared for Utana is not an ordinary nurse. Actually, I don't believe there is such a thing as an "ordinary nurse." What I mean to say is that this nurse, Cheryl, has exceptional experience. She has seen it all! During her thirty-nine-year career, not only has she worked intensive care, emergency room, and hospice, but she has been a top gun flight nurse. Therefore, for Cheryl, who has been at the bedside of many dying patients, to be so impressed by Utana's last moments, is highly significant.

She first met Utana in the hospital. As Cheryl entered her room, she sensed that this was a special patient. Even Utana's name was unique. She was named for the legendary princess.

The story tells of a Ute Indian Princess, Utana, who loved a young brave, Timpanac. When Timpanac died, the devastated Utana climbed a mountain, lay down, and died. One can visualize her shape while looking up at Mount Timpanogos in Utah. The legend concludes that their united hearts are hanging inside the Timpanogos cave.

Cheryl's Utana was also dying. She had advanced colon cancer. Her two daughters had flown in to take her home. As they sat by their mother's hospital bed, they looked to Cheryl for the assurance that they could do this thing—that they could keep their mother comfortable at home. Cheryl smiled as if to say, "Oh yes, my dear ladies, your mother will find the comfort you want for her, in her own home, and in your caring arms."

Cheryl made the necessary arrangements: discharge orders, medications, supplies, and equipment. She even had a hospital bed set up in Utana's living room. When all was ready, Utana was gratefully taken home. Cheryl helped tuck her in, fussing with the covers, making sure she was comfortable. Cheryl returned frequently, knowing that the end was near.

It wasn't just clinical experience that led Cheryl to a short prognosis. Soon after returning home, Utana began talking about seeing a flickering light by the piano. Such descriptions are not uncommon when death is imminent. Cheryl knew this.

She said, "Having heard these kind of reports from dying people before, I had a pretty fair idea that the end was near."

However, what actually happened surprised even this experienced nurse. Cheryl explained, "I was standing on her left, and she was asleep. And I just stood there and watched her for a few seconds . . . and suddenly she opened her eyes . . . and she turned her head to the right and looked upwards . . . and suddenly the most beautiful, incredible smile of astonishment and joy came over this woman's face."

The daughters were only a few steps away in the kitchen. Cheryl called out softly, "Ladies, come quickly, she's leaving us." Both daughters arrived in time to see the amazing expression on their mother's face. Cheryl continued, "It [the expression] lingered there for maybe three or four seconds, and then it slowly faded away . . . and the light left her eyes . . . and she passed on."

Cheryl said, "It was as if someone, visible only to Utana, reached out and took her spiritual hand and led her to the other side."

Like Utana of the Timpanogos legend, this Utana left a lasting impression on those who knew and loved her. They will never forget Utana and her final smile—a smile foretelling of forever and of a future filled with joy.

chapter

Richard

Doctor Ira Byock has written an amazing book called "The Four Things That Matter Most." According to Dr. Byock, the four things are actually four statements: "Please forgive me. I forgive you. Thank you. I love you."

He continues, "Ask a man who is being wheeled into transplant surgery or a woman facing chemotherapy for the third time what's on his or her mind, and the answer will always involve the people they love. Always."

Richard's story demonstrates that miracles can occur to facilitate the saying of these four phrases. In Richard's case, such a miracle occurred because Dr. Byock was absolutely right: hearing and saying, "Please forgive me," and "I forgive you," mattered most.

The nurse, Wendy, first met Richard when she was sent to admit him into hospice. Eighty-six-year-old Richard lived in a charming rambler home, made even more charming by Peggy, his artistic wife. But hidden behind all the beauty and charm was a profound sadness. Many years earlier Richard had an affair. His wife was very hurt, and so were the children—especially Kent.

Kent could never forget this image: He had walked into a restaurant with his wife one evening and unexpectedly saw his father with another woman. Kent was torn between the love he felt for his mother and the respect he wished he could feel for his dad. It was more than he could bear. So he avoided his father for years—for twenty-five years.

In his younger days, Richard was a dynamic businessman. As he grew older, Kent and his brother took over the day-to-day management of their father's business. Eventually Richard developed Alzheimer's disease. This disease, and additional health issues, progressed until the doctor suggested hospice.

Richard—a large, weakened man—stayed in bed until afternoon. At about two o'clock, he would go into the kitchen, eat some cereal, and then move to the outside porch or to a recliner until dinner. Richard was back in bed by six.

Dementia patients often develop a fear of water. Richard was no exception. He tried to avoid anything to do with water, including the shower. He refused to let the hospice aide bathe him. However, James—a hospice social worker—established a feeling of trust and eventually persuaded Richard to get into the shower, much to the satisfaction of Richard's wife.

Richard wanted to visit some of the local stores that he owned. So James agreed to take Richard to visit his businesses. Peggy told Richard to get dressed several times. Richard finally went into the bedroom and returned wearing his suit coat and sweat pants. Frustrated, she told him to go change his clothes. He returned shortly wearing a sweatshirt and suit pants . . . and off they went.

Richard seemed to recognize and enjoy seeing his old workplaces. James dedicated time each week for these excursions. Occasionally they would run into Richard's son, Kent. Kent never acknowledged Richard. He would walk past him, looking straight ahead, get into his truck, and drive away.

Winter was approaching, and Peggy decided to take Richard to stay at their winter home in a warmer part of the country. Wendy helped the family transfer Richard to another hospice. She often wondered how they were getting along. She wondered if she would ever see them again.

In March, the snowbirds returned, and, once again, Wendy was Richard's nurse. But Richard had changed . . . significantly.

Peggy told Wendy that she took Richard into their old bathroom, and he couldn't remember how to stand up. She said, "I had a terrible time getting him back into bed."

The next day Wendy assisted Richard into the kitchen for his standard bowl of cereal. He couldn't remember how to eat. He began to cry. He said, "I don't know what is going on." He continued to sob over and over, "I don't know what to do! I don't know what to do!"

Wendy called a family meeting. She suggested to Peggy, their two daughters, and one of the sons (Kent refused to attend), that they should consider placing Richard into an assisted living center. Everyone agreed. The children apologized for Kent's lack of interest and attendance. "He has unresolved issues," they explained.

The first day in the assisted living center was hard. Richard never got out of bed. On days two to four he managed to move about the facility. Within one week Richard began to die. The severity of his dementia had increased to this expected terminal stage. Wendy now visited Richard daily.

On Friday morning Wendy called Peggy. "Richard's oxygen saturation level is only in the fifties. His heart rate is rapid at one hundred thirty to one hundred forty beats per minute. I can't get a blood pressure. I don't think he'll make it through the night."

But Richard did live through the night. By then he hadn't been responsive for almost forty-eight hours. When Wendy returned to the assisted living center, Peggy, and three of the children were at the bedside. Wendy was grateful that Richard had family by his side. But she was keenly aware of an ever-present feeling of sadness caused by the unresolved issue.

And then it happened! Kent walked into the room! Amazing! To their further amazement, Richard opened his eyes and called Kent by name! Kent walked over to his dad's bedside, knelt down, took his father's hand in his, and tearfully told his dad that he was sorry for all those lost years— twenty-five lost years! Richard said that he was so sorry for what had happened and thanked Kent for his forgiveness.

Without saying a word, Wendy—followed by Peggy and the other three children—left the room. They all knew that Kent needed some time alone with his dad. After a precious reunion, Kent went to the foyer to get the rest of his family. When they re-entered the room, Richard was once again in a coma-like unresponsive state. He died peacefully three hours later.

Kent hugged Wendy and thanked her for bringing them together.

When joyfully remembering this miracle, Wendy said, "I wasn't responsible for bringing this family together; it was a force far greater than me, and a father and son saying the two things that mattered most. "I'm sorry" and "I forgive."

chapter

Rose

The hospice nurse, Nancy, assisted the mortician as he took Rose's body out the doorway and proceeded towards the van. The family followed. They had supported each other so well during Rose's illness, and they continued to stay close during this difficult departure.

As Nancy steadied the wheeled stretcher, keeping a steady eye on the ground, she suddenly heard simultaneous sobs burst forth from the family walking a few steps behind her. Startled, she turned to see what was causing their intense cries and desperately asked, "What?"

Two months earlier Nancy had been asked to take over the care of this young patient named Rose. A previous nurse had told Rose that if she wanted to die, all she had to do was to stop eating and drinking. And Rose wanted to die. A neurological disease had left her helpless and completely dependent.

Rose had three young children, ages two to seven. She was totally devoted to them. As long as she could, she pampered them with stories and homemade meals. But the illness was brutal and relentless. Rose became increasingly weak. One day she could no longer walk.

Eventually she was confined to the bedroom. When caregivers tried to shield her from the boisterous children, Rose insisted that her little ones be allowed to climb upon her bed and sit by her side. They were more important to her than her own comfort.

As Nancy entered Rose's bedroom for the first time, she knew what she had to do. She must be very matter-of-fact. Rose was dealing with serious issues. There could be no wasted time.

"Rose, you must eat. You must drink. I know you don't want to be a burden. I know you want to free your family of this struggle, but you can't—you mustn't—die this way."

As an experienced hospice nurse, Nancy understood that our bodies know how to die. When it is time for death to occur, a new set of physiological rules takes over. Patients no longer experience hunger and thirst. But Rose still had some precious time left. Forcing herself to stop eating and drinking prematurely was only making her miserable.

Nancy put a glass to Rose's lips. Rose trusted this new nurse, this Nancy. She began to drink, gently at first. Then she began to gulp the water as it flowed down her dry starving throat.

Relieved, Rose's family finally relaxed in the background. At long last, this nightmare of forcibly freeing the family was over. Rose would die when the time was right. And Nancy would protect her.

Every week, and sometimes more often, Nancy would make the pilgrimage to Rose's home. She answered questions. She solved problems. She coordinated services with Rose's hospice team which included the medical director, a chaplain, a social worker, and nurses' aides. She dried tears, and she shed tears.

Eventually the time was right. During her last few days, Rose didn't want any food or drink. Yet, she was comfortable. She slipped into a comatose-like state. No longer did she move or speak. However—amazingly—whenever her children entered the room, tears would stream down from her eyes.

These tears had a profound impact on Nancy.

Kind and watchful neighbors, ever aware of the changes occurring, helped care for the children. Now, with the end just a few moments away, the children were called close. Rose always loved having them close.

Rose's mother and father were at the bedside, supporting Rose and their son-in-law. Nancy came. She pronounced Rose's death. She hugged this family. And she stayed. For no matter how prepared a family may be, when the mortician takes a loved one's body away from the arms which have so tenderly provided care . . . well . . . it is always difficult.

After the family had some time to grieve together, the mortician arrived. He offered his sympathy and answered questions. He suggested a time for Rose's husband to come by and make further arrangements. And then he lifted Rose's limp body onto the stretcher and respectfully placed a cover. Someone opened the door, and they all—including the children—proceeded outside.

Then came the unexpected sobs from the family walking behind her.

"Look! Look Nancy! Look up!"

Nancy looked up and saw a huge glorious rainbow right in front of the house.

The excited family began to explain.

Several weeks earlier Rose had pulled the children close and told them, 'Mommy must go away. But when I go, I promise that I will send you a gift. I will send you a rainbow so that you will know that I love you, and that I am watching over you.

Mommy will always be watching over you."

Rose loved rainbows.

But on the day Rose died, there was no rain in the forecast. It was a sunny day in this land of high desert. The hospice medical director, Dr. Gary, explained what had happened. He had been outside at a ballgame, when, out of nowhere, a most unusual storm arose. Due to the storm's intensity, the ballgame was halted. But the rain only lasted a few minutes. And then, with the sun shining bright, a most brilliant rainbow settled over the valley.

And that was the rainbow that settled over Rose's children. It still glows today in each of their hearts, reminding them of their mother's undying love.

chapter

Kate

To me, it looked like Kate would die very soon. Her tiny emaciated body lay helpless in the dark room that she shared with several other patients. Carol, her daughter, turned in my direction and asked, "Can I take her home? Will you help us?"

"Yes," I replied. "We will work together as a team. You won't be alone."

Carol was relieved. Actually, I knew that she would let nothing stand in the way of bringing her mother home. She wanted her mother to be surrounded by those who loved her.

Carol had previously finished her basement and made it into an apartment for Kate. However, Kate would not be going to the apartment. I had a special bed delivered and assembled in a first floor room.

Soon after arriving home, Kate refused to eat. She wasn't hungry. She refused all but a few sips of water. She wasn't thirsty. She had entered the active dying process. I visited her every day.

This family had inherited some land that overlooked a small town. They called their land Johnson's Hill. Carol and her husband had built their home in the center of Johnson's Hill. Kate and her husband had had many children. Several of Carol's brothers and sisters also lived on the hill. The various family members, including moms and dads, brothers and sisters, cousins and more cousins, came by frequently. It was easy. They were close. It was natural. They had always supported each other.

I learned a lot from spending time at Carol's home. They had an extremely high quality of life. They had everything that truly matters: companionship, happiness, safety, support, fun—all blessings that resulted from their closeness. Not only were they physically close, they were emotionally, socially, and spiritually connected. Their bonds ran deep.

Kate was a queen to this family; little, frail, emaciated, but still revered as the wonderful mother who had given them life, home, and family. We attended to Kate's every need.

As each day passed, Kate became weaker.

One day, Carol asked me if I would like to see the basement apartment where Kate used to live prior to her illness. I was interested, and we went downstairs. It was an ideal living space with plenty of light. After the tour, Carol and I returned to Kate's bedside. Kate promptly chastised us by saying, "I'm dying, don't leave me!" We never ventured too far again.

As the week drew to a close, Kate's breathing was shallow and faint. She could no longer move. We changed her position periodically to enhance her comfort. The hospice medical director ordered concentrated morphine so that we could control any discomfort. Since Kate could no longer swallow, we would draw up a small amount of water into a syringe and place it under her tongue as needed.

Kate slipped into a deep sleep. She seemed non-responsive to our puttering about the room. However, on several occasions when a cherished grandchild would enter, Kate opened her eyes. As the child stood close, I could hear her weakened voice rationing chosen words, lavishing praise, and calling each one by name.

Kate entered into a coma, and our charting reflected this assessment. We continued to turn Kate and administer to her hygiene needs. Digestion is not a priority in actively dying patients, and intake ceases. Therefore, at this stage, the need to change briefs is minimal. It's amazing how the natural process respects and facilitates a peaceful closure.

The afternoon prior to Kate's death, I leaned over her still body to wipe her forehead. As I did so, she opened her eyes one last time, looked directly at me (I was very close), and faintly, yet powerfully, spoke the following, "You must teach . . . advise . . . and carefully instruct." After delivering the message, she immediately slipped back into her previous state.

I will never forget Kate. I attended to her body following her death. I tried, as do all hospice staff, to provide some emotional support and comfort for the family. However, as so often happens, they comforted me. When I left their home that final time, they offered me a white shawl, handmade by Kate. Yet, Kate had already given me two treasured gifts: a sacred message from above, and a glimpse into heaven on earth.

chapter 11

María

I first saw María as she sat in a nursing center dining room with her family. I was impressed with her beautiful eyes and the devotion of her family. We were not able to communicate very clearly as they spoke only Spanish. I would need to arrange for a translator. At that time I didn't realize that she would be one of my most challenging and difficult hospice cases.

The facility medical director was sending María home with our hospice. María was suffering from end-stage liver disease classified as nonalcoholic cirrhosis.

María was excited to be going home. I made arrangements for a hospital bed and other equipment. My next visit occurred in their tiny rented apartment.

María's husband had recently lost his job. The translator told me that his supervisor didn't like working with non-English speaking employees, and so he had fired him. He was concerned about how to pay the rent. Our social worker assisted him in applying for unemployment compensation.

As I examined María, it became evident that María's ascites (fluid that fills the abdomen) was worsening. The ascites was causing abdominal distension. In studying her past history, I learned that she had been given a paracentesis (insertion of a thin tube or catheter into the abdomen to drain excess fluid) whenever the swelling became severe.

María did not believe she was dying, and her family, including her extended family, made it clear that they were determined to help her recover. María was weak and unsteady, but she wanted to get out of the hospital bed. Without hesitation, her adult son went to her side and gently assisted her to move about the room. I admired his love and support. I admired the devotion of this family. However, I knew that, due to her advanced condition, recovery was not a realistic option.

María wanted to accomplish some goals with her family. Some of her goals could be met in a relatively short time, and I was anxious to give her that time.

As the ascites advanced, María's abdominal swelling became severe. I called her primary care doctor to see if he would arrange for another paracentesis—at least one more—so that she could enjoy a bit more time at home and complete a few of her cherished family goals.

The doctor refused.

I understood his perspective as he explained that the fluid would simply return again. I already knew that following the immediate relief from a paracentesis, there is an eventual re-accumulation of fluid.

But still, I was disappointed.

As I hung up the phone, reality hit. There was no postponing the challenge. The fluid would continue to build, swelling María's abdomen to the point that the pain and dyspnea (difficult breathing) would become intolerable.

We would have only a few days to prepare María for death. First I attempted to explain the situation, with María's hospice aide, Cecilia, serving as translator. Cecilia had been bathing María on a daily basis, and María trusted her. However, María refused to believe that recovery wasn't an option.

I discussed the difficult situation with our hospice medical director. He speaks fluent Spanish. He offered to meet me at the patient's home and explain the situation.

I arrived a few minutes after our doctor had finished speaking with María and her family. María was crying. There were crumpled tear-filled tissues strewn about the room, and the family was very upset. They were in denial. They didn't want to believe that María would die soon.

A kind woman from the extended family pulled me aside. In broken English she explained that the doctor had been very kind and sensitive.

Although María and her family said that they would not give up hope, she decided to give away her modest treasures. That very afternoon I watched as she sat on the hospital bed and passed out token gifts to her loved ones. She knew—in spite of family denial, she knew.

From that day forward, María required more medication to help her tolerate severe abdominal pain. As the levels of medication increased, the level of her consciousness decreased. And, as often happens with liver failure, body toxins and an inability to process ammonia were likewise causing decreased cognition. María was moving into a coma.

Cecilia and I went every day. We cared for both María and her family. María began to actively die. The son, who so tenderly looked after his mother, worked the night shift. He felt he had to continue going to work so that the rent would get paid. But how he hated to leave his mother!

One day I informed the family that María would probably die that afternoon or evening. María's son went to work and explained to his boss that his mother was dying. The boss insisted that he stay until he completed his cleaning duties as janitor.

All the family gathered in the little room around María's bed. I stayed by their side. The denial was over. They were ready to have María free from earthly trials.

But María seemed to be lingering longer than expected. So many times we thought that she had taken her last breath, only to see her resume breathing.

My heart ached for her devoted son. I knew it was tearing his heart apart to not be with her. Her breathing was slow, labored and shallow. The apnea was consistent and extensive.

But still she continued to linger.

And then a miracle happened! In the wee hours of the morning, as María's son finally walked through her door, she took her very last breath. All eyes were fixed upon him. As difficult as it was for him to see that last breath and lose his angel mother, he was there! No words can describe how much that meant to him!

Was it just a coincidence that she died as he arrived? I don't think so.

As a hospice nurse, I've come to expect such "little" miracles. These miracles occur frequently during the course of our work—so frequently that I know I can rely on an unseen force or unseen angels to fill in the gaps, to smooth out what I cannot, and to sprinkle a loved one's passing with love.

And what further amazes me is that heaven seems to be able to clearly distinguish and ascertain what the truest needs are. Time and time again I see evidence that supports these words found in holy writ: "Precious in the sight of the Lord is the death of his saints." (Psalm 116:15)

And so it was for María . . . and so it was for her son.

chapter 12

Rafaela

Rafaela's story begins and ends with windows.
Rafaela lived with her son and daughter-in-law.
Their home, situated on a fairly busy town street,
was very pleasant. But I was surprised to see, upon
my first visit, that all the windows were covered with
tightly closed blinds. The daughter-in-law, Cindy,
explained that if the blinds were open, Rafaela
would become extremely agitated by the outdoor
activity. And so, to eliminate a source of frustration,
the windows remained covered at all times.

Rafaela had Alzheimer's disease, and she was
entering the latter stages of dementia.

One day Cindy couldn't find her. Rafaela had
made it to the street and was using a white
handkerchief to flag down a ride. She was angry
about needing to take a shower. She was angry about

needing to get dressed. She had had enough. She decided to leave. Rafaela was not happy when Cindy insisted she come inside. Rafaela scolded Cindy, and Cindy was grateful that she couldn't understand Spanish, Rafaela's language!

Rafaela was pleasant with me. But there were times when she was difficult with Cindy. Cindy tended to Rafaela's every need. There were times when Cindy was physically and emotionally exhausted. Her life had become centered around Rafaela. Cooking, bathing, dressing, cleaning, supervision, hygiene—all these tasks were performed by Cindy. I would bring in additional help so that Cindy could relax and more fully enjoy their remaining time together.

On my first visit, Rafaela gently reached out and touched my face. I looked into her eyes and knew that she was a special patient. Rafaela only spoke Spanish, and my Spanish was limited to a few words. Nevertheless, I wanted to provide optimal care for her.

Alzheimer's is a most challenging terminal illness. I knew I would need to provide significant teaching. Transitions are hard, for as dementia patients lose the ability to be in control, they are often unaware of the extent of their disability. They don't understand that they can no longer be in control.

Transitions are also hard for caregivers who are caught up in an overwhelmingly difficult situation and don't realize that eventually that stage and situation will pass.

One day Rafaela removed her brief and flushed it down the toilet. Of course this caused a major incident with flooding in the bathroom. The overflow demanded significant attention from Cindy, which delighted Rafaela. She thought it was quite funny. Her daughter-in-law was not amused, at least not at that time. Eventually she also had a good laugh.

Learning to look at the humorous side of this disease seemed to help Rafaela's family.

I told them about one of my dementia patients who had called 911 and reported a dead body in the house. The daughter tried to explain, but the summoned police insisted on searching their entire house. Several months later that same patient called out the fire department. There was no fire. Eventually the community began to catch on.

I shared other examples of humorous experiences. I had several patients in a locked dementia unit. One day as I was charting behind the nurse's station, the facility nurse sat at a feeding table between two dementia patients. She gave several bites to one patient and then turned and fed the other patient. When her back was to the patient on her left, that patient picked up his glass of ice water and poured it down her back. Was she ever surprised!

Judy Seegmiller, in her book *Living with Big Al* tells about the time when her husband, an Alzheimer's patient, turned to her in bed and asked who she was. She responded by telling him that she was his wife.

He said, "Boy, that's a relief!"

On another occasion he looked at her bare feet and asked, "What are those?"

"Those are my feet," she answered.

He replied, "Those are the ugliest things I ever saw."

Once when an aide came to bathe one of our dementia patients, the patient put her foot in the toilet, mistaking the toilet for the bathtub. The patient yelled, "Oh, the bath water is ice cold!" Our aide redirected her, kindly suggesting that she bathe in the bigger bathtub with the warmer water!

In spite of the humor associated with this disease, the stages of dementia become increasingly brutal. A window to the soul seems to close when a patient can no longer remember their beloved family members. In the final stage of dementia, patients often lose the ability to speak, smile, and even hold up their head.

We try to finds ways to reach them.

Cindy played music that Rafaela enjoyed. Dementia patients usually respond positively to music. When an activity director is sensitive to patient needs, I often hear old-fashioned background music lifting the mood of the facility. This is beneficial for all patients, dementia or otherwise. One of my recent dementia patients couldn't speak, but when I would sing a song from his generation, he would join in, remembering perfectly much of the lyrics.

As these patients get closer to death, sometimes a window opens, a window of sublime clarity. A patient, who hasn't recognized a family member, may suddenly call that family member by name. Or perhaps a patient, who hasn't spoken in some time, may make a profound statement.

Such was the case with Rafaela. A few days before her death, Rafaela turned to Cindy, and using perfect English, looked deeply into Cindy's eyes and said, "I'm going to have to go." To Cindy, this tender and miraculous acknowledgement signified that Rafaela knew her departure would bring about a lonely space. Rafaela cared, and it seemed as if a guardian angel helped her share her concern with Cindy.

And so, windows close and windows open. Sometimes the window remains open for just a few seconds. But, within those few seconds, a soul sees into the beyond.

And isn't that what windows are for?

chapter

Glen

While end-of-life experiences are often filled with love, inspiration, and miracles, occasionally I am even more inspired by the events of life itself.

In the fall of 2009 I knocked on the door of one of my former patients, Glen C. Barratt. Dolores, his widow, opened the door and invited me in. I asked if I could tell the story of her deceased husband.

Several years earlier, when asked to arrange Glen's hospice service, I didn't realize that he was one of the first liberating American soldiers to enter Dachau, the first Nazi concentration camp.

On the day of his admission to hospice, Dolores and I sat with him in their kitchen. I checked Glen's blood pressure, respirations, temperature, and heart. His physical heart could no longer function as it once had, but his inner heart was noble and true.

Caring for war veterans is not unusual for nurses. We lose these great heroes to death on a daily basis. One thing I firmly believe: to serve one's country is an act of great love and service, and is regarded highly in heaven.

I include Glen's unique story as a tribute to all of our brave veterans, living and dead.

Glen was a reconnaissance officer in McArthur's 242 Infantry 42nd "Rainbow" Division under General Harry Collins.

Glen stated, "Because of the notoriety of the 42nd Division, the Germans knew where we were at all times on the ocean. When we arrived in Marseille in southern France, our division . . . was assigned to General Clark's army . . . Our destination was Strasbourg . . . When we finally arrived, I went in, threw down my bedroll in the pitch dark room, and, when I woke in the morning, there was a dead German soldier in the room with me."

Glen talked about being sent to the front in December. ". . . we were assigned to the front lines—the French town of Hatten. We many times had to stay with French families . . . The 25th Panzer Division (German) attacked our division . . . I remember the German soldiers were dressed in white and were hiding behind the tanks and tried to look like the snow . . . The battle continued for almost a week . . . I recall coming back to where I had slept the night before . . . The house had been hit by a bomb . . . The French woman, when I found her (she already had one arm off), I saw the bomb had severed her other arm . . . She lived, but the real sad thing about it was that her two children had been hit and blown to pieces all over the room on my bedroll and my baggage.

". . . I recall two days later going into the town of Hatten at night trying to locate where the enemy was. I recall crawling through the snow to within 50 feet of some German troops . . . This was a long, tough week —our worst fight—but we pushed the Germans back across the Rhine River."

Glen was also assigned to a portion of the Haguenau forest. ". . . every night we dug fox holes and threw dirt over them . . . This enabled us to sleep and be somewhat protected from mortar fire. Many of the men contracted trench foot, which was caused from having cold, wet feet for so long . . . The roads were steep and mountainous. The battle offenses along the Modar River were Hitler's final stand.

"One of our many missions was to search the mountains for SS officers, the most dangerous of Hitler's army. About this time, our baby was due at home . . . I sat on a tombstone and read the telegram Dad had sent. I had a beautiful baby girl.

"Since it was my job to always find the front lines and report back to Captain Caringola, I recall going into the city of Wurzburg. I walked into the city and down the street and found no one alive. It was an eerie quiet. All the people who lived there were now dead or hiding. It was a weird feeling to see a dead city.

"Our unit, as we approached Munich, observed the German resistance was lighter. From then on . . . Captain told me to proceed to Dachau. I arrived there one of the first soldiers . . . At this point I hadn't realized how cruel humans could be. What I saw there I would hope no one would ever have to see . . . It was my duty to be there first because of my job.

"I've been in a place where the spirit and influence of God was missing, and I can assure you it's a lonely and frightening place. The captives were thin and starving. I opened the first boxcar. I saw dead naked bodies stacked like cordwood."

Years later Glen visited with a woman who was one of the liberated Jewish prisoners. As an eighteen-year-old college student, she was arrested and sent to Dachau. Glen stated, "We recounted the scenes at that camp, the dead bodies ready to be burned in the furnace, the captives starving, the dead bodies in the moot surrounding the camp . . . Her last request to me was, 'warn people that this can happen.'"

A 1945 Associated Press article by Louis P. Lochner, entitled, "This Camp Shows Yanks Nazi Horror" stated, "Every soldier, officer, and war correspondent attached to the 42nd (Rainbow) Division of the U.S. Seventh Army today had one word seared into his soul— Dachau."

Lochner continued, "Here human beings were experimented on as though they were guinea pigs, were eliminated by slow starvation, and their bodies burned wholesale in a gigantic crematory. Thirty-five railway cars loaded with corpses emaciated literally to skin and bones are lined up outside the camp."

He also reported, "In the crematory there was a stench that made the strongest men turn pale and flee to the outside for air. In two rooms of this institution were naked human bodies, bearing the signs of horrible torture and piled to the ceiling. The SS (Elite Guard) guards had been unable to complete their task of burning the emaciated bodies, though they worked . . . at it day and night."

Glen himself reported, "You see, the Nazis tried to wipe out not only the Jews, but also the physically handicapped . . . and people who didn't agree politically."

According to Wikipedia, not only was Dachau established by the National Socialist Party and the German Nationalist People's Party, but Heinrich Himmler, Chief of Police of Munich, officially described the camp as "the first concentration camp for political prisoners." Of Dachau's over 200,000 prisoners, about one-third were Jews, but the greater number—two-thirds—were political prisoners.

Lochner was more than right, those sixty-five years ago. The horrors of the National Socialist (Nazi) Party were "seared" into the hearts of our fighting men. I've listened to them on dying beds, with nothing to gain, open their hearts and share first-hand accounts of savagery, depravity, and inhumanity.

Glen kept a carefully preserved quote from Curtis R. Whiteway, 99th Infantry Division, Plainfield, VT, "I tell the kids about how precious freedom is . . . about how we must learn from the past . . . And I tell them that, as a soldier in World War II, I had the opportunity to fight for freedom and that they have to keep that freedom through their everyday actions . . . about how they have to speak up . . ."

In conclusion Glen stated, "The German army was the best trained army the world had ever seen. A real war machine. But still, they couldn't stand up to the Americans. We had the ability to produce weapons and oil, and nothing could match the patriotism of our soldiers.

"I remember how happy I was in March of 1946, when I was given orders to be sent home . . . what a feeling it was to enter New York Harbor; to look up and see the beautiful Statue of Liberty and the beautiful buildings of New York. I had spent one and a half years in total darkness at night. Lights of the city and being back in the U.S.A. brought tears of joy to me and many other soldiers returning home."

Glen was a true man. He was true to his country, to his lovely wife and family, and to freedom's cause.

I've held Glen's hand. I've held other hands, hands once strong in battle, now weak and wrinkled, but boldly testifying of freedom's fragility. I have no excuse. Whenever human liberties are threatened, I will remember Glen's valiant service. I must speak up! Freedom is not free!

Note: In August of 1945 Glen was awarded the Bronze Star Medal for Meritorious achievement in action on 10-11 January 1945, near Hatten, France. Leading a reconnaissance mission to establish contact with two platoons that had been cut off by an enemy attack, Lieutenant Barratt made his way through heavy fire into Hatten. There he determined that the friendly troops in the town were completely isolated. Proceeding into Rittershofen, Lieutenant Barratt searched for friendly troops there, finding and rescuing those who had evaded the enemy penetration. His escape route cut by infiltrating Germans, Lieutenant Barratt led his party to safety by an alternate route. His courage, leadership, and initiative resulted in the rescue of a large number of men. Entered military service from American Fork, Utah.

A note of thank-you: I'd like to extend a special thank-you to Glen's angel wife, Dolores Barratt, for permitting me to share his story. I'd also like to thank Glen's son, Mark H. Barratt who encouraged Glen to record his experiences. Mark is the author of the inspiring series, "The Guardian of Heaven."

chapter 14

Home Alone

Were you ever lost? When you were a young child did you ever wander away in a crowded place, perhaps in a store?

Did you want to cry out, "Mom! Dad!"

Did your parents ever leave you somewhere?

Do you remember how you felt? Were you afraid? Did you feel panic?

Death is especially hard on children. Not only do they experience profound grief, but they are lost. A trusted protector is gone! They are alone! What is going to happen? There is a bit of a child in all of us. Please remember to be especially kind to a grieving child. The child is not only grieving, the child is lost.

Here is my story:

The loud recess bell echoed throughout the schoolyard. Instantly, the jump rope pulled through my fingers as my playmates turned to race back to class. Left alone, I started to run, but somehow, something was different. I seemed to be separated from the others. I had entered a kind of slow motion. It was as if someone—someone very intent—was standing over me watching my every move, and I was somehow aware of their perspective. I can still see my body round the corner with my small feet pounding on the concrete driveway as I ran toward the school building. I had no way of knowing that within the next few minutes, life would come along, pick me up and mercilessly throw me into a cold existence where I would be forced to learn what it means to be home alone without my dad, mom, grandma, or brother.

Kids poured into their seats. Our class smelled of outdoor sweat. As usual, the teacher let us take turns going out in the hall for a drink from the fountain. I held my small hand tightly around the cold steel to let as much water as possible slip down my throat before returning. I never got enough. Things were just starting to return to normal; books and paper out, pencils in hand—then came a knock at the door.

The class was curious and relieved for a break, but this was an unusual interruption. It was not another teacher or the principal. It was my neighbor. She stood at the door talking to the teacher, who turned to my direction.

"Candace, come here."

I stood up and went to the teacher. She walked away.

My neighbor was now in charge, and she asked me, "Where is your coat and lunch box?"

We walked around the corner and I pulled my coat off the hanger and put it on. I was going somewhere. When I turned to take my first steps toward the outside, she told me the unthinkable. She told me my dad had died that morning.

My mind revolted. *No! No! This can't be!*

With an agonizing yelp of pain, life rolled over, exposing a still, bare underside. Shortly after Dad's funeral, President Kennedy was assassinated. That week there were no shows on TV, only blood and funerals, guns and death, Kennedy and Oswald. After Dad's funeral Mom gave our dog away. He had belonged to Dad and was now seen as an unnecessary expense. When a distant cousin drove away with our dog, I stood there, saying nothing. I remember standing by the window, staring outside. I watched two sisters playing, and I tried to understand why.

Homecomings, once filled with excited voices and mouth-watering smells such as simmering soups and fried chicken, were replaced by a profoundly quiet, dark nothingness. Earlier, the year had taken my only brother away to college and grandma to a nursing home. Now, with Dad gone, Mom was forced to leave home to find whatever jobs she could. And she did find them. There was the maid position at the "old folks home." I spent Saturdays and summers watching the elderly while Mom cleaned up after them. The worst job was the hospital cafeteria position. Mom had to be there early, so she would drop me off at my neighbors before sunrise. I would sit there in the dark until they woke up. Sometimes their mother would give me a piece of hot toast covered with real butter. I liked the taste.

After school, our house was empty and cold. Money was tight, so the thermostat was turned down. I ate alone. Some nights I took bologna and squeezed it between white bread until it was completely flat, or I would open a can of cold baked beans and eat them with bread. I ate and remembered mealtimes with all of us at the table and Mom standing by the stove cooking pancakes, and visits where my cousins and I played while our dads talked, and vacations with Dad driving and singing "Nothing could be finer than to be in Carolina," and—my favorite—his bedtime stories. After Dad's story, I would lie in bed and listen to laughter and voices coming from downstairs.

After Dad's funeral, I prayed that when Mom and I went to bed, no armed attacker would break into our house. I was scared. I never wanted to go to sleep.

But I did go to sleep. And I did wake up. And I learned from Dad's death and from life's other side.

Now life has rolled over for me a second time. Homecomings are warm again. There are voices, meals, and lighted rooms. Today I came home and found every light on in the house. I did not complain. I'll never forget what it was like to be home alone.

chapter

15

Mother

There is a cardboard box that sits under my desk. It's a nice box. It has a lid—the kind of box that copy paper comes in. But I don't open it. I keep it close, but I don't open it. It contains memories that are too tender to touch.

When I first brought it home, it sat there for a full year before I could open it. One day I felt I had to reach inside. Time was going by, and I needed to write Mom's story.

The box contained the last of Mom's things I had gathered together. There were pictures, a journal, a calendar with notes in her handwriting—even a poem she kept about me.

Yes, it's a good box. I keep it close, but I don't open it—very often.

The end began with a call. I was busy getting ready for our flight to our favorite vacation spot in North Carolina. "Honey, don't forget to pack your swimsuit," I reminded my husband, as the phone rang.

My only brother, Robert, was calling. "Mom had a fall last night. She was on the floor until early this morning, when she crawled to the pull-light for help. She's in the hospital. Candy, I don't think she can continue to live alone."

My mind was spinning. "When we get to North Carolina tomorrow, I'll rent a car and drive up."

Robert was relieved. He knew that, as a hospice nurse, I understood such issues. As a mother, I had come to expect miracles. The timing of Mom's fall enabled me to go to her. A miracle. I was her only daughter. Mom hated that I lived so far away in the west.

The long drive to Pennsylvania was even longer due to a jam on the Washington D. C. beltway. I finally showed up at Mom's apartment where Robert and his wife Phyllis were camped-out on the sofa bed. Their pillows and blankets looked comforting. In fact, Mom's place was always comforting.

I fell asleep in Mom's bed. In the morning, I felt anxious to get to the hospital. Mom looked so frail with IVs in her bruised arm. She weighed less than a hundred pounds. She smiled as I gave her a kiss. "I love you, Mom."

A doctor entered and, while standing by Mom's bed, announced that she could no longer live independently. "You need to move to an assisted living facility."

What power! In less than five minutes, this doctor had redefined Mom's life. Always an obedient one, my mother agreed.

Robert and I went to find the best situation for Mom. Too many people use up all their savings on fine assisted living. Then when they need more help, they are forced to settle for an inferior long-term facility. We would not let that happen to Mom.

We checked out several places.

As we returned to the hospital, the discharge planner called. "I've found a vacancy in Martinsburg. This place also has a long-term care unit, so your mother will never need to transfer."

As we updated Mom, she looked concerned. Her life was about to change.

I drove with Robert to the new facility. We were impressed with the lobby and administrative offices. We were disappointed in the assisted living area. The hall was dreary and narrow. The tiny room Mom would share had very little natural light. Pipes ran across the low ceiling.

But we had no other good option. With my bad back, I couldn't give Mom the care she would need, and Mom refused to impose on Robert.

I spent the rest of the day at the hospital with Mom. After she went to sleep, I returned to her apartment.

Robert was already there. "Candy, I want you to go through some of Mom's things and take what you want."

I entered the kitchen, sat down on the floor, and opened a bottom drawer. There was Mom's wooden rolling pin. I picked it up and held it, not wanting to let go. It represented the best of times. The day might be dreary, cold, and wet outside, but inside, Mom's kitchen was happy, warm, and filled with tempting smells of fresh hot rolls and pies in the making. As a young girl, I stood eye-level with the old table, looking up as Mom created tasty delights using the rolling pin. I knew we were important because Mom took such joy in feeding us.

"Take it," Robert said, "take it."

Emotion welled up. I felt grateful that he wanted me to have it, but felt despair at saying good-bye to Mom, bit by bit, piece by piece. Tears formed. At first I cried softly, silently. But soon, as I sat there on the floor, rolling pin in hand, my brother by my side, the tears wouldn't stop, and they flooded my eyes. I cried like a baby.

Life would never be the same. We would never return to Mom's apartment. We would never again spread butter over a warm roll from Mom's oven or bite into one of her perfect pies. The end had begun.

This trip to Pennsylvania reminded me of another "piggy-back" trip the previous summer. I had been working for a large hospice. In August they sent me to Cincinnati for a conference. When it was over, I hopped into a rental car and drove to Indiana to visit my daughter for a few hours. Afterwards, at around ten thirty, I began the drive to Pennsylvania to visit Mom. I drove all night, sleeping for two hours in a New Stanton McDonald's parking lot. I awoke and found a strange looking man peering at me through my closed car window.

"Are you ok?" he shouted.

Startled and only half awake, I nodded. He turned and walked away.

I arrived just in time to attend a discharge meeting. Mom was temporarily staying in a rehabilitation facility following a hospital stay.

My brother hadn't told Mom that I would be at the meeting. In fact, we set her up for the surprise. I called Robert earlier that day, and he gave Mom the phone. I pretended to be far away. "Hi Mom, how's everything in Pennsylvania?" A few hours later, as I entered the room, my eighty-four-year-old mother looked in my direction. When she realized that I was there, that it was really me, she began to shake and cry from pure joy. It was frightening for her to have her fate discussed in such a meeting. She was so glad that I was there. And so was I.

If I had had my way, that discharge meeting would have never been necessary.

Robert had called in July to report that Mom had a high fever with confusion, weakness and coma-like lethargy. "Candy, Mom's neighbors called me to come. She's been lying on the couch for two days. When we try to wake her, she only mumbles incoherently. She looks like she's dying!"

"She is dying, Robert. I'm sure that she has another UTI that has turned septic. Let's call in a hospice team, I'll fly back, and we will let Mom die comfortably and peacefully." I was willing, even anxious, to let her go. A few years earlier, the drug Vioxx had caused Mom to have a series of strokes. Since the strokes, Mom had very little quality of life. In her weakened state, just trying to open the fridge caused her pain.

Extensive nursing experience told me it was in Mom's best interest to let her die peacefully—now! But I was out west, and Mom was back east. My sister-in-law, Phyllis, felt she should be taken to the hospital—now! 911 was called. This subsequent discharge meeting was the last time Mom would be permitted to return to her apartment. Her decline continued steadily, predictably, and unmercifully.

When Mom first went to live in the tiny room in the assisted living ward, I was able to call her everyday. In October I promised her that I would come for a week during the holidays. Such a promise always made her happy.

The facility had a small guest room in the basement. There were no hotels in that rural part of Pennsylvania. The guest room made it possible for me to make the most of the time I had with Mom—another miracle! I arrived late. The night nurse walked me down the long dark hall to the guest room. Every other light fixture was turned off to economize. All doors were tightly closed. But I had an entire week to spend with Mom!

I borrowed a wheelchair and took Mom out everyday. I'd drive around and get as close to the back door as possible so that it was easier for her to get into the car. One day, I took Mom and an old friend out to lunch. Mom had become so tiny that she couldn't sit at the booth. We took our coats, wrapped them into one, and helped Mom get on top of the coats.

In the facility, Mom used a walker to get around. She didn't go far. She was fearful of getting lost. She knew how to get to the lunchroom, and that was far enough. The doors were too hard for her to open, so she never went outside alone.

Mom's brother made a long trip to visit while I was there. What a highlight for Mom. He brought some fresh fruit and lovingly fed it to her. He and I both cried as he left to return home. Leaving Mom was always hard. She never wanted you to go.

By spring Mom had declined significantly. She had developed compression fractures and required more pain medicine. As osteoporosis advances, a simple sneeze can cause bones in the spine to break. Mom was moved into a skilled nursing unit and put on hospice.

Robert called, "Mom has been talking about her mother and father coming. She also said, 'There are all these people in heaven. You just don't know.'"

Robert gave his cell phone to Mom, and I was able to tell her I loved her. This was the only way Mom and I could talk. She could no longer answer the phone. I could no longer call her every day; another piece lost, another bit gone—little things never retrieved.

Before this decline, I would call Mom every morning. I began making daily calls when the Vioxx strokes rendered her unable to drive. We looked forward to each call. I had a habit of sitting on the bathroom counter when putting on makeup. I'd grab the speakerphone, prop it up just right, and we could talk while I applied eyeliner, blush, lipstick, etc.

One day my husband walked by as I was doing this daily ritual, and he said, "What are you going to do when you are too stiff to crawl up there?"

I laughed and replied, "Are you expecting me to get old soon?"

But there was something prophetic about his odd question. Something devastating was coming.

On May tenth, I woke my husband at four o'clock in the morning and told him that I couldn't move. He thought I had hurt my back. He lifted me to the floor, thinking that a firmer surface would help. But it didn't. Pain restricted every move.

X-rays revealed two herniated disks. However, the doctor felt that arthritis was causing most of my pain. I didn't believe him. "How can somebody go to bed feeling fine and wake the next day with severe arthritis?" I asked. He didn't answer.

Another doctor sent me to a lab where blood was taken from my arm. "Your sed rate (a indicator of inflammation) is very high. You're not crazy. Something serious is going on."

I knew he was right. I was spending all morning just getting washed and dressed. Afterwards, I spent my days lying on the couch, packed in ice. We put ice packs behind my back and on my neck and shoulders.

Oh those shoulders! Eventually both of my shoulders froze. I used a laptop computer to frantically search disease patterns. The thought of lingering for years, gradually losing more and more function horrified me.

The doctor sent me for more tests. He was checking for bone cancer, rheumatoid arthritis, ankylosing spondylitis—anything. Each test came back unremarkable. I had none of those diseases. Finally, ruling out all other possibilities, he seriously gave me his best diagnosis. "I believe you have polymyalgia."

"What's polymyalgia?"

He answered, "It's a form of arthritis. You can go to bed perfectly fine, and wake the next day very ill. Your immune system attacks your own muscles. Polymyalgia can also cause blindness, aneurysm, and strokes." He handed me a pamphlet and recommended steroid medication.

"I don't want to take steroids."

He agreed, but only if regular blood tests showed improvement.

Previously I had purchased a ticket to fly to Pennsylvania in June, with my daughter and son-in-law, who wanted to see Mom. But could I make the trip? There were times when my husband had to lift me over steps just a few inches high. Dennis, my son-in-law, declared that unless I needed a diaper change, I could still make the trip.

Desperate to see Mom, I decided to go.

After the flight, when we finally arrived in Martinsburg, I was so stiff from sitting all day that I couldn't get out of the rental car. My daughter, Gayla, crawled into the back seat behind me and, using her leg muscles, pushed me up and out the door. She and I began to laugh because it seemed so bizarre. "They're going to think I'm here to be admitted!"

But Dennis was not laughing. He looked quite concerned.

I was shocked to see Mom's situation. She was no longer allowed to ambulate independently. They were putting her into a wheelchair every morning, with an alarm attached to her back. If she attempted to rise, the alarm would blast in her ears. Aides attached it to her nightgown when she went to bed at night. She was afraid to turn over in bed, due to the alarm.

"I mustn't move," she declared with crippling fear.

I told Robert what she had said.

"Mom once told me she was in prison," he replied. "You can see how she would think that."

I asked the hospice to get her a lower bed and allow her to move independently. Forced prolonged sitting made her anxious and increased her pain. The nurses were giving her Ativan two to four times each day. When I was by her side, she could walk over fifty feet. I wanted her to be granted freedom to move instead of forced confinement and drugs.

The facility said that they had a "no restraint" policy. But this loud and frightening alarm attached to the back of a woman who still had the capability to stand and walk was a restraint, nonetheless.

I wasn't the only one concerned. Mom had noticed my illness. One day she said, "You walk stiff." She began to cry and added, "I don't want you to be sick!"

Mom's aide told me, "One day when I arrived to shower your mother, she articulately asked me, 'Would you please leave and return after my husband has gone?'" This was curious. My father had died when I was only nine years old. Was medication interfering with her cognition, or were we seeing a pattern? Hospice patients often speak of visits from deceased family.

Eventually I had to return home. The facility reported that Mom was never able to reestablish the ability to ambulate independently. Upon hearing this report, I requested that the hospice get her a wheelchair fitted to her size. Her arthritic hands couldn't move a wheelchair, but I knew she could putter around the hall by propelling herself with her feet. They agreed. I was relieved. I discovered much later that the requested wheelchair never arrived. On my next visit, I found her legs dangling hopelessly above the floor.

In May of 2006 a call came announcing that Mom had a broken hip. The doctor recommended surgery, even though he didn't think Mom would survive. She did. I flew back to help her recover.

Mom's room was at the darker end of a long hall. As I once again walked down the hall to Mom's room, I saw the familiar faces of patients—patients lying in bed, patients sitting in wheelchairs, patients in distress. What would I find when I walked through my mother's door, I wondered?

In the hall, Sarah, a tiny white haired woman, was calling out, "Oh, I don't know where I am! Oh, I don't know where I am! Do you know where I am?" She never stopped calling those words, day-to-day, week-to-week, and month-to-month. The aides would move her from one end of the hall to the other, so no one had to listen continuously. But you could still hear Sarah crying out, somewhere in the distance.

Bertha was sitting in her room with a towel draped over her face, like a bird whose cage gets covered up at night. When the nurses removed her towel to feed her, she would begin a high-pitched scream, which permeated the entire ward. "Yea ya yea ya yea ya yeaaaaaaaaaaa! Yea ya yea ya yea ya yeaaaaaaaaaaa! Yea ya yea ya yea ya yeaaaaaaaaaaa!"

"Bertha! Hush now!" an aide would occasionally chide.

But Bertha only quieted when the towel was once again hung over her face.

Finally I approached Mom's room. Her name and her picture were posted on the door. It was a picture taken when she first moved to the facility. In it she was sitting up in a regular chair. Such a picture would never again be possible. This picture of what once was haunted me.

I cautiously, timidly entered the room, worried, wondering what I would see. Mom was in there, flat on her back, a huge wedge pillow spreading her tiny legs in an attempt to prevent an incapacitating post-surgical contracture.

She was asleep. It was a deep sleep, the kind of sleep from which one never fully recovers; a sleep that comes over patients and begins to pull them into another realm, only releasing them occasionally so goodbyes can be given to those they love.

Mom was very lethargic. I went to her bedside, knelt down, and said, "Mom, I love you. It's Candy. I love you, Mom." I kissed her soft fragile face. I hoped, but I didn't know if she understood I was there. She tried to respond. I could see her facial muscles move slightly as if she was trying to speak.

Wednesday she roused a bit, even smiled, but she never said my name. In the afternoon aides lifted her out of bed and put her in a wheelchair. Then they left the room. It was just Mom and me. Almost immediately she began to stress with increasing pain. "Oh! Oh! Ouch, Ouch, Ouch!" Her face turned towards me, her eyes frantically searching for mine! What could I do?

I had repeatedly asked for medication to keep her out of pain. Even in sleep I could see her brow furrow. And whenever the aides came in to turn Mom, she would moan and cry. But she was required to wait. Even the hospice was not allowed to adjust a medication order without the approval of some mysterious pharmacy representative. The charge nurse was angry with me for my repeated appeals. "I'm very busy here," she said in exasperation.

"Help me, Jesus!" I found myself desperately pleading out loud.

And then a thought came into my mind. I could ask for her to have a blessing. I quickly went to the nursing station and asked that break-thru pain medication be given as soon as possible. Then I made a call. Soon two of the most blessed looking young men, respectfully dressed in suits, arrived to give Mom the requested blessing.

By this time Mom was again lying on her bed. They placed their hands upon her head. Tenderly calling her by her full name, she was told that she was an elect daughter of God. Many comforting words were offered. She was blessed to be at peace, as her body prepared to leave this mortal existence. Immediately following the blessing, she looked into my eyes and declared, "My mother is by my side." I believed her.

Mom used to sometimes call me "Darling." The morning of my departure, Mom spoke—she said, "Oh Darling!" In those two emotion filled words, she was saying, "I know you are here. I love you! Oh how I don't want you to leave." She was saying things that matter most. I understood. I'll forever cherish the memory of, "Oh Darling!"

I wouldn't leave until the hospice reluctantly complied with my wish for a reclining wheelchair—

one which would give her head support and be much more comfortable.

Several months later the hospice called me to announce that they were taking Mom "off service."

"She has become chronic," the doctor said.

Those were devastating words. Her quality of life would take another dive. The personal hospice aide would no longer visit. The personal hospice nurse would no longer come. Mom couldn't and wouldn't understand.

She was wheelchair bound.

"Please make sure the special hospice wheelchair is replaced with one of the reclining wheelchairs in the facility."

The hospice agreed. I had observed several such chairs lined up against the wall. When hospice pulls out, so goes the equipment.

In June of 2007, I flew into Baltimore on a Saturday and drove to my brother's home in Dover, PA. My sister-in-law had melanoma. It began with a small black spot, the size of a pencil eraser.

"It's confined to the leg," declared the doctor. "We can tourniquet your leg, infuse it with ten times the normal strength of chemo, and wipe out the cancer. We've had great success with this treatment."

Thankful to have a viable option, Robert and Phyllis agreed. But their insurance didn't. "You're request for treatment is denied. You can appeal."

The initial request and long appeal process stole valuable time from Phyllis. As a nurse, I knew the wait was destroying her chances. Melanoma moves fast.

After the appeal denial, Robert took out a second mortgage to finance the treatment. The doctor offered to perform the procedure free of charge, but the hospital's fees would be enormous. A cashier's check was sent overnight express to the hospital. The hospital refused to schedule the procedure for two more weeks.

"How can a cashier's check not be good?" my brother asked in desperation.

"Sorry, that's our policy!"

Following the procedure, tumors began to disappear from Phyllis's leg. Hope! But eventually the tumors returned with a vengeance.

"Delay probably caused the failure," said the doctor. "We could amputate your leg and buy you time."

"No," said Phyllis, "I will keep my leg."

But her leg was severely compromised. Chemotherapy had injured tissues, especially in her foot. She could no longer drive. She never complained.

She walked with a cane.

Robert and Phyllis were glad to see me. Phyllis had worked all day to make their home as inviting as possible. It was too much for her. That night she became ill. I could hear her throwing up in the bathroom.

The bathroom became a place of ritualistic importance as each day Phyllis managed to get into the bathtub. She would carefully remove each bandage from her leg and spray her wounds with water, removing some of the rotting flesh and exudates.

Witnessing this bizarre bandage ritual added another dimension to my trip. Lessons can be learned by watching a loved one lose a part of their body. I've heard it said, "We are not physical beings here for a spiritual experience, we are spiritual beings here for a physical experience." Phyllis graciously dealt with her intense physical experience. Tumors overtook her leg. A putrid smell permeated their home.

"Robert," I said privately, "Phyllis will soon be gone. When she gets on the other side and finds out how wonderful it is, she may come back for Mom—soon."

On Sunday I went with Robert and Phyllis to the church where Robert is a pastor. Then I drove the many miles to be with Mom.

Entering, I pushed the button that released the door into the full-care unit. Once again I walked down the long hall. As usual, Sarah was calling out, "Oh, I don't know where I am!"

Passing Bertha's room I saw her silently sitting with a towel draped over her head.

I smiled at a nurse sitting at the nurse's station. I had become familiar to the staff. Some were glad to see me. Some would be glad when I left. Fans on the wall were blowing out continuously, circulating stale air. Someone had had an "accident" and would need a diaper change.

A group of patients were lined up in wheelchairs across from the nurse's station. The most interesting activity here was watching nurses and aides. Patients grew to care about each nurse and aide who scurried about, trying—trying to keep up.

At the end of the group I spied Mother. Cautiously I approached. Would she know me? I knelt down by her wheelchair. She stared at me silently, intently, but never said my name—another piece gone. I found a folding chair and placed it next to Mom. Now I was the end of the line. I felt content just to be by her side, to know life as she lived it, to share her existence for a precious and perhaps last time. This had become her world—the bizarre world of the aged—the world known by names such as Long-term Care, Nursing Home, Skilled Nursing Facility, and Old-folks Home. Blessedly, she seemed at peace.

Mom was wheeled into a small dining room for dinner. Each night after dinner I drove to a local dairy and bought their favorite ice cream for everyone at Mom's table. I fed Mom. Her body had become contracted. She tried to reach her mouth, but her hands were tightly turned permanently inward.

The promised reclining wheelchair was nowhere to be found. Mom had become so contracted from leaning all day in a standard wheelchair that when we lay her in her bed her head continued to be elevated above the pillow. It took about fifteen minutes before her neck could partially relax. Her arms had become permanently contracted from an effort to keep warm. Those fans! She was sitting below those fans!

I called hospice and explained that Mom had declined. She was, without doubt, eligible. Hospice returned and once again brought in a more appropriate wheelchair.

I came to love the understaffed and overworked aides and nurses who cared for Mom. They did their best.

I also loved Nellie. Growing up, Nellie was our neighbor. On Thursdays, our school bus made an extra stop in front of the old community center. Nellie was inside with a big flannel graph board. We children would pour into the room, find a seat, and watch as Nellie made stories from holy writ come alive. We were inspired with priceless faith.

Nellie was there again when, at age nine, I lost my dad to a massive heart attack. Our family became instantly poor. Mom got a job and had to leave for work before dawn. Nellie kept her back door unlocked so I would have a warm place to wait for the school bus. She offered me warm, buttered toast every morning.

Nellie, now in her eighties, had moved to the village's independent living section. She showed up daily to visit Mom. Some of Mom's pants had become torn. When I showed Nellie the worn pants, she disappeared with them. The next morning I found the pants on Mom's bedside table, each pair sewed perfectly.

A few months later, on an early day in September as I was checking messages, I heard my brother sobbing into the answering machine. Phyllis had just died. We knew this news was coming. Robert had been calling me daily about her. I flew back to support him. He didn't know I was coming, so my return was a welcome surprise. I saw true and deep gratitude in his eyes. I cried as we chose her favorite songs to be sung at the funeral. After the funeral, I went to visit Mom.

Common things sometimes happen together. Perhaps God decides what needs to be learned at each stage of life. Repetition is the key to learning. Anyway, I've come to learn that the angels have an amazing system of organization.

Mom had developed a slight wheeze. I begged the hospice, "Please don't allow anyone to give her an antibiotic and force her to linger longer in her contracted emaciated body! If and when this wheeze progresses, keep her comfortable, but please don't add anything unnatural."

It was so good to see the familiar faces of Mom's caregivers. They had become family. It was good to have hospice again. Probably only those who have lost a loved one understand how much it means to look into the eyes of a hospice team and see compassion.

After a week, Susan, Mom's hospice nurse, said, "Go home." She understood that my family back west also needed me. I didn't want to leave Mom's side. I believed that Phyllis would soon come to get Mom. Susan assured me that she would let me know when it was time to come again.

That call came in less than a month. "Thank-you, Susan."

Susan called me on Tuesday, October 2nd. "Your mother is actively dying. You need to come."

"I'll get a flight today," I assured her.

Family was notified. I realized that in less than one month my brother would bury both his wife and his mother. I quickly threw some clothes into a small suitcase. I looked at each of my drawers. Did I forget anything? My daughter, Holly, drove me to the airport. Family is everything.

I took a flight into Baltimore, picked up the rental car, and drove three hours to Martinsburg. I walked into Mom's room, took her hand, and said, "Mom, its Candy. I'm here."

Mom opened her eyes and tried to answer me. I knew. She knew.

Wednesday passed peacefully. My brother and I were able to spend some precious time together and with Mom. I didn't want to leave her side, but since her oxygen saturations were holding steady, Robert encouraged me to sleep in the guest room.

Thursday I went to the basement storage room and took out Mom's box. All her worldly possessions were in that box. Our ever-thoughtful mother had purchased a ruffled pink blouse to wear at her funeral. I found the blouse neatly folded just as she had placed it in the box. There was a professional picture taken of her wearing that pink blouse, which she had taken for the newspaper. She even gave me a sample obituary to use as a guide. She made everything as easy as possible.

I spent Thursday and Friday by her side. I kept her mouth moist and applied chap stick to her lips. I put cool washcloths on her forehead. I requested morphine whenever she seemed anxious. I told her over and over how much I loved her. I began to clean out her room and pack up her belongings. Some things would go to Robert. Some things would go home with me. I knew it would be much more difficult for me to do this once her spirit was gone. I tried to get as much done as possible.

On Friday Robert needed to return to Dover. I knew I would miss him, but perhaps Mother wanted to spare him her final hours. Her passing seemed long in coming. I wasn't happy that oxygen had been started prior to my arrival. The hospice nurse apologized for whoever had disregarded my wishes about such intervention. I knew the oxygen was making the labor of dying more difficult. Rather than risk a conflict, I began gradually turning the oxygen down.

At noon, Leann, my coworker and a great hospice nurse, called to check on how I was doing. I held the phone close to Mom so Leann could hear her breathing. "Candy, patients do not live more than twelve hours when they sound like that," she advised.

I sat alone by Mom's side. Finally I completely silenced the noisy oxygen concentrator. Within a few minutes, the Director of Nursing (DON) came to Mom's room. Someone had reported what was considered my "indiscretion." I quietly explained that I felt aggressive interventions make it difficult to die naturally.

She replied, "I agree, but how do we get others to understand?"

A blessed acquittal!

That afternoon Susan, Mom's hospice nurse, arrived. She stayed with me for several hours. We knew it would be soon, but eventually—and reluctantly—she had to leave. Her family had come to pick her up, and she invited them in. They carried in the cutest puppy. Their visit provided a bit of miraculous and needed relief—a specific relief, wisely chosen.

The day shift aides stopped by to say goodbye. They knew that they would never see Mom again. I had come to know them well. They will be forever in my heart. There were days when we joked together as they changed beds and changed diapers—kind experts of change as they care for those about to make an ultimate transition.

I remember one aide who simply put his hand on my shoulder. He had tears in his eyes. He didn't need to say anything. I began to cry. This was a sacred moment. He shared my grief and carried some of it home. Mom's minister came by, at my suggestion, and offered a tender prayer.

At dinnertime I ate a few bites from Mom's tray. She had long ago quit eating.

I expected to spend the evening alone with Mother, when my cousin, Joann, entered the doorway. How welcome she was! Her own mother had died recently, and due to the memories of her mother's death, it was very difficult for her to come. But she came! I needed her and her visit. Mother had always said that Joann's mother was one of the nicest, kindest people in this world. Joann stayed with me until bedtime.

The facility was beginning to wind down for the evening. Gradually, the unit became quieter as each patient was put to bed. I didn't want to leave Mom's side—not now. Mom was still breathing about twenty times each minute. I pulled two chairs together and was preparing to sleep next to Mom's bed, when a nurse's aide came in with Mom's roommate. This roommate had always tried to look out for Mother. She was very hard of hearing, and she flipped on the TV and blasted the sound. She didn't realize how close death was.

My hopes for a quiet night with Mom were gone. I stretched out next to Mother and held her hand. The night nurse walked into the room, stretched out her hands and rubbed Mom's head, ruffling her white hair. I had never seen anyone do that before, but it felt right. I was glad she had touched Mom. I was glad that we shared that moment. Then she turned and left the room.

At exactly eleven pm, Mom paused after a breath. "Mom!"

Mom took one more partial breath—then nothing.

"Mom, Mom, Mom!" I tried to call her back! I didn't expect her to go like this! Not now! Not like this! It was supposed to be quiet! There was supposed to be a gradual slowing of her breathing! Panic filled my cries! "Mom!"

"I'm so sorry dear . . ."

Those words sounded strange coming from Mom's roommate and over the noisy TV.

Yes, mother was gone! And, in spite of all my training, in spite of all my experience, I wasn't ready. I wasn't prepared. I was shocked at how hard it was to have her leave. It was as if the angels had picked eleven pm as the time to sweep her up in their arms and carry her back home, and at exactly eleven pm they carried out their plan—regardless of how many breaths she was taking, regardless of how noisy the room had become.

I don't remember how she knew—did I call out?—but the head-rubbing nurse entered the room to confirm Mom's death. I called Robert and my family. Two unknown aides arrived to respectfully clean and dress Mom's body. I stayed to help. If there had been a catheter or IV line in use, the nurse would have discontinued all such equipment.

A hospice representative never came. Mom died on the late shift, so I had never previously met the staff on duty. I longed for a familiar face. I was thankful that the mortician was understanding and had respectfully dressed in a suit.

After he left, I went down the long dark basement hall that leads to the guest room. I couldn't sleep. I couldn't stop crying. Could this be real? Was Mother really gone? I called my husband. "Bob, I need you. Please come." He promised that he would arrive as soon as possible.

At about four in the morning, exhaustion finally caught up with me and forced me to get some restless sleep.

Saturday morning Nellie came to my door with some orange juice.

Robert called and asked me to go to the florist and select flowers. He instructed, "Get flowers from the grandchildren and from us. And Candy, there is something else. I'd like you to have two white roses placed on a heart for Mom to hold."

"Ok," I replied.

"Candy," he added, "the two white roses will represent you and me."

That sweet thought made me cry aloud. And I cried in and out of the next few days.

Many dear ones came to the viewing and funeral. My husband stood by my side. Robert stood alone. Each kind visitor had shared a part of Mom's life.

One of the busy aides took time to come and see Mother one last time. Robert and I will forever appreciate their support. We love their generous spirits.

And Robert, may I tell you how much I love you! I admire your courage, I enjoy your company, and I am proud that you are my brother.

Maybe that's why Mom was willing to linger in an ailing body. Angels knew her long departure would pull us together. With each of her losses, she gave us an inheritance of love—an inheritance that will enrich our relationship forever.

To you, to each of you who have read these words, "Thank-you!" I feel a connection with you. Whoever you are, truly we can be as one, as life teaches us lessons to last for eternity.

And Mom, "Thank-you!" I will forever be in your debt. I forever remain your daughter . . . your "darling" daughter.

chapter 16

Hospice Inspiration

To hold a hand
To end a pain
To whisper a name with love
To see into eyes and understand heart
To do more, give more, and be more
Through touch alone
To share everything and feel all
This is our work, our mission, our inspiration.

Candy Kinser

chapter 17

Benjamin

I was not a nurse when Benjamin died. I was just another mother who learned about losing a child from Teresa's profound and heartfelt words.

The Circle

In this passing of time, I, who
Was once a young girl, have aged into an old
Woman, wise with sorrow and experience. Standing,
I knead this bread, and listening to the sparrows sing
This early morn, I am remembering my
Babe, who was my joy and his father's son and a
brother also.

When fall readies us for winter, he came,
Jubilant, into our arms. So easy a birth,
I felt almost guilty, and I cried from the happiness
This boy gave.

And we called him Benjamin, the one
With clear blue eyes and easy smile
With auburn hair curled round a fingertip, just so,
Skin so soft and sweet, like the down in a
Newly-made nest.

No anguish, he gave, only harmony to our hurried
Lives. He taught us to go slow, to savor each
Minute memory of every moment, to remember
And to never forget.

A late winter night settled over us;
The baby in restless sleep.
An angel waiting by his bed to take
The small, willing hand, and call him home, so soon.
We despaired but we were comforted
And this small blessing has been ours—
One to guide our actions and be ever-present in the
Thoughts we hold.

I have no regrets, but at times I sorrow
And think of things that might have been;

Of a boy who played with trucks, ate french fries
With lots of ketchup, sold worms, and flew a
Kite in March winds.

Yet his mission is far greater now
And I know when it's my turn to depart, he'll take
my hand
And lead me as once I did him.
For in all passing,
There is sweetness still.

Teresa Davenport

(Used by permission)

chapter 18

My Father-In-Law

My father-in-law was a master clock smith by profession. Following his funeral, as we bowed our heads to pray, the grandfather clock that he assembled suddenly began to chime. To our family it was as if he was giving us a tender farewell.

His Last Goodbye

As we journey back to our home to rest,
And the long road continues on,
Row by row, and house by house
The homes of men go by.

Was it just another simple house
Where we traveled home to be,

Or a heaven on earth he built just for us
Before his time to leave?

The walls of blue held true
As they welcomed us through the years,
And held once again our family dear
When we came to shed our tears.

We alone did not cry . . .
All heaven seemed to shake.
And the clouds came low, as they understood
The great man they came to take.

His hands touched each of us, one by one
As we struggled through the years
They blessed our heads on fevered beds,
And cradled our young ones near.

With mom by his side he spared us
From want, and cold, and care.
He gave us pride in our family name
And an eternal home to share.

And when his hands had finished their work,
And we bowed our heads at noon,
The clock tolled out his last goodbye
While the rarest of rainbows shone through.

Now it's up to us to carry on
In a manner he would bless
As he bids goodbye through chimes and sky
While journeying to his heavenly rest.

chapter

Lizzy

It is difficult to lose a friend—especially one who has made a significant difference in the quality of your life. I lost such a friend twice: once when we moved away, and again when she died unexpectedly, and oh so young.

Dear Ones,

I didn't know Liz was ill until this past Friday, when Annette told me. How shocked, utterly shocked I was. The tears flowed and still flow. Oh Charlie, how thankful I will always be that you found a girl named Liz, and that you brought this angel girl to live near us. Liz impacted my life like a raging storm of lightning—the light being the divine light of Christ. The warm sweet showers that resulted gave me life, light, and living water. Indeed, I have the life I have today because of Liz and her abundant miraculous love and spiritual understanding. Heaven must have had a supreme need, a need so profound and unique that only Liz could fill. For she truly is one in a million—no—there is no other female that could ever be what Liz has been to so many. Liz had the strength of ten women. I have no doubt that she could have overcome any physical illness—but divine intervention dictated otherwise. How I pray for your dear family. I can't imagine what a loss! Again heaven must know that you each have the strength to endure that which would crush many other families. But you are not any other family. You are the Charlie Sherwood family. You are everything amazing. How we thank the Lord that it was once our privilege to walk the floors of your home. Bob just held me close when we received the news. What could he say? There are no words that can express how much an angel will be missed. I wish, oh how I wish, that she were still on this earth. I remember a poem Liz wrote. Several weeks ago I read it during a training meeting. Many individuals came up and requested a copy. I hope you don't mind. At the time, I had no idea that this poem, written by my dear friend Lizzy, was a premonition, if you will, of a not-so-distant day:

In a not so distant day
We will stand side by side
Perhaps hand in hand
As daughters of our Heavenly Father
And look into the face
Of our brother Jesus Christ.
We will then realize how well we know Him,
How much we have missed Him,
And how deeply we love Him.
When He extends
His loving arms to us,
And calls us by name,
We will know
That every step we took on the path back to Him
Was as precious
As each drop of blood He shed for us.
He is our Saviour, our Friend, our Redeemer.

Elizabeth L. Sherwood

(Used by permission)

I love you Liz. Please know how I love you! Love, hugs, and tears from a forever friend,

- Candy Kinser

chapter

Ike's Poem

I had the sweet experience of caring for a brave grandfather with Alzheimer's disease. When he passed away, his family found comfort in a poem shared by his granddaughter, Danielle.

Freedom Within

Don't worry about me for now I am free
The memories of my life that I had long forgotten
They are all coming back—my wonderful life.
I am no longer in pain, stuck within myself,
unable to remember
Smiling down from Heaven, I can think clearly
My beautiful wife—I love you—
Don't you worry about me

For I will always be by your side
instead of just a shell
My wonderful children—my love for each of you
Was always in my heart
Now I can recall everything that I could not before
Life is fleeting—but my memories now
Will never disappear
Remember the good times—all the smiles we shared
And for all my grandchildren: Guess What?
Grandpa loves you!
I remember it all—this disease did not win—
My love will never fade

(Used by permission)

chapter 21

Walking With Angels

Expect miracles! Expect a miracle today! Why? Because you are part of a great work! Each of us—patients and caregivers—come together, united in our purpose to make the most out of each and every day.

As we seek to appreciate and serve in the present, we please the great giver of all good gifts, who promises to comfort and to love each of His children.

Pure service is to visit one another in our afflictions. As the door of each home opens, so opens a door to love, service, and fellowship.

Thank you, patients! You permit us to experience the joy of giving.

Thank you, families! You invite us into your home where you live and serve and love one another. Your home is a bit of heaven on earth.

Thank you, staff! You are an essential part of a specialty team dedicated to lifting and lightening burdens.

Expect the help of angels as you participate in this great work. Indeed, many have been the days when an impossible schedule just works out, when a patient says just what one needed to hear, when a family member meets a simple need with exceptional love and strength given them by an unseen force.

Although usually unseen, angels are among us, helping us, lifting us in our united effort to bless one another.

Holy writ declares, "Come, ye blessed . . . For I was an hungered, and ye gave me meat: I was thirsty, and ye gave me drink: I was a stranger, and ye took me in: Naked, and ye clothed me: I was sick, and ye visited me . . ." (Matt. 25:34-36)

When you reach out your hand and touch the hand of another, angels rejoice. They have no greater work than to help the children of God help one another. The individual is everything!

Thank you for opening the door and extending an opportunity to walk with angels as we reach out our hands and touch one another. From the beginning to the end of life, from Alpha to Omega, the angels walk among us. We are not alone!

"Precious in the sight of the Lord is the death of his saints." (Psalms 116: 15)

No one expresses it better than in the immortal writings of Henry Van Dyke:

Gone From My Sight

I am standing upon the seashore. A ship at my side spreads her white sails to the moving breeze and starts for the blue ocean. She is an object of beauty and strength. I stand and watch her until, at length, she hangs like a speck of white cloud just where the sea and sky come to mingle with each other.

Then someone at my side says, "There, she is gone."

Gone where?

Gone from my sight. That is all. She is just as large in mast, hull, and spar as she was when she left my side. And she is just as able to bear her load of living freight to her destined port.

Her diminished size is in me—not in her. And just at the moment when someone says, "There, she is gone," there are other eyes watching her coming, and other voices ready to take up the glad shout, "Here she comes!"

And that is dying.

Henry Van Dyke

chapter

Paradise

Yes, that is dying.

But as you can probably see by now, dying isn't really dying at all. It's not the end of everything—as witnessed by so many of my patients during their final moments here on earth.

Of course, our bodies *do* die. Upon reaching the end of their natural and beautiful end-of-life process, we *will* be separated from our bodies for a time.

But we live on! Death is just the beginning of living again. Believe it! Embrace it! There is a beautiful place awaiting us called Paradise.

Allow me to conclude with this very special eye-witness account of a patient who has actually been there . . . and lived to tell about it.

I first met the patient, Evan Chidester, when I was called to the hospital to discuss hospice with him. His daughter, Rose, was by his side. I was impressed with the love and deep respect she had for her father. During our visit, Evan told me that he had died previously—not once, but twice.

Evan lived a life of service to his family, church, and community. He was a scoutmaster for over fifteen years. He had a strong drive to function as fully as possible, which was a challenge because his left leg had been amputated.

Just prior to his actual death on June 16, 2012, he told Rose that his grandfather had been there multiple times over the preceding weeks. Evan said, "Grandpa comes, and he comforts me."

It is an honor to share Evan's amazing story.

From the Pen of Evan Leroy Chidester

On September 1, 1986, I left my home in Springville, Utah on my Honda Aspencade motorcycle. It was a beautiful day, so I decided to ride south to the town of Nephi, then cross the mountains to Mt. Pleasant. From there I traveled north to Thistle Junction where the road meets Highway 6 running from Provo to Price.

I stopped at the stop sign at Thistle Junction and was waiting for traffic to clear so I could turn left onto Highway 6 and continue down the canyon to Springville and home. As I was watching traffic go by, I noticed a camper that had passed in front of me that was swaying very erratically.

From that point, I don't remember much until nearly three months later when I heard my boy David's voice. I asked him, "What has happened to me?" He answered saying, "You've been in a wreck, and you have lost your leg. But you will be all right."

Some time later, after I fully regained consciousness, I was told that a girl who had been speeding passed a truck on the right side and had hit me broadside at sixty-five miles per hour, and that my motorcycle and I both flew up over the top of her car and fell back on the highway. My left leg was crushed badly just below the knee, both of my hands were broken, also my right wrist. I had a skull fracture above my left eye, my left hip was broken in three places, and my back was broken. I took forty units of blood in the first twenty-four hours after I was taken to the hospital. I have had a total of eighteen surgeries and received eighty-seven units of blood to enable me to survive and walk again.

I make mention of this accident and that I was in the hospital for seven and a half months to help the reader understand more fully why I had the experiences I now share with you. I only share these experiences in the hope that they will serve to strengthen your testimony and faith in God the Eternal Father and in His Son, Jesus Christ.

The second day I was in the hospital, I had an aneurism hit my lungs, and I died for about seven and a half minutes. Suddenly I had the sensation of floating above the doctors and nurses who were around my bed in the intensive care unit. I remember hearing a very annoying sound like heavy equipment grinding away. Next I found myself inside what seemed like a very dark tunnel. As I entered the tunnel, I heard a voice calling for angels to attend me. I cannot describe the tunnel, as it was very dark. I also had the sensation of traveling at a tremendous speed. I was not frightened or overly concerned. I only had the feeling that I was where I should be, and that all was well.

It was not long before I saw a small speck of light ahead of me, and as I continued on, the light got larger and larger. When I reached the end of the tunnel, the light was coming from an archway. I no more stepped out into this bright light, not even having time to look around, when a rather tall man stepped in front of me and held out his hand as if to shake my hand. I reached out to shake his hand, and he took me by the hand and placed his other hand on my shoulder and turned me around facing the tunnel and told me, "You have to go back now."

I then found myself traveling back through the tunnel in the opposite direction. Soon I approached the hospital and came back into the intensive care unit where I watched the doctors insert a long hypodermic needle into my chest. Then I heard him tell the nurse to charge the paddles. He placed them on either side of my chest, and I re-entered my body.

From that time on, I don't remember anything because I was unconscious and heavily sedated. I slipped in and out of consciousness for two and a half months.

My bishop (James M. Rawle), who worked at the hospital as a biochemist, had kept a close watch over me. He had to leave town to attend a seminar and feared that I wouldn't be alive when he returned. So he laid his hand on me and gave me another blessing before leaving to attend the seminar.

A short time later, the doctors came to the conclusion that they could not save my leg. The infections and toxins throughout my lower leg would cost me my life if they didn't amputate. And yet they feared that I did not have the strength to survive the operation to amputate my leg.

My family gathered for a family prayer and determined to have the doctors remove my leg, despite the risks. Because of the concern over the surgery, another blessing was pronounced upon my head. Monte Atwood anointed, and my son-in-law sealed and blessed me to have the strength to survive the surgery.

Some later time, I experienced leaving my body for the second time. I found myself traveling again in that long dark tunnel. I continued on until I came out into a place that was beautiful beyond description. The light was extremely bright—so bright that I don't have words to describe it. I found myself standing on a beautiful pathway that was made of small round stones about an inch and a half around. They were fitted together perfectly, and the path was as smooth as a tabletop. There were three different colors of stone. Some were ivory, some were tan, and some were light brown. The stones looked as though they were held together with some kind of bonding material.

After looking at the pathway, I looked down and realized that I had a leg on my left side. My leg was there, just as if it had never been amputated. My body was whole, and my leg had no injury of any kind.

I then looked in front of me into a magnificent bed of flowers. They were a bright red, although I had never seen that shade of red before. I recognized them—they were tulips. The bed of red tulips covered about two acres. Beyond the red tulips was a bed of white ones, then a bed of yellow, and beyond the yellow, a bed of purple. Instead of being about ten inches high, they were over two feet high. And the flower itself was about six inches across and about seven inches deep. I was amazed at their beauty.

I was standing by a tree, and even though the leaves were green, I had never seen that shade of green anywhere on earth. Each leaf was perfectly formed. I reached over and pulled a leaf down to observe it. It looked almost as if it were made of plastic that had been dipped in glass, then polished to a high shine. Nevertheless it was a living leaf.

I then turned my attention again to the tulips, and as I looked down at one, I asked in my mind, "How can a flower grow to be so large and beautiful?" As if in answer to the question in my mind, the bright light that was all around me just seemed to focus and concentrate on that flower until it was transparent and I could see right into the innermost parts of the flower. I could see it bringing up moisture and nourishment and watched the whole process. When my mind was satisfied, the light just withdrew, and I found myself looking at the flower as before.

I then turned my attention to some beautiful flowers that were on a small mound and looked to be about a city block away. I thought in my mind again, "I would like to go over and observe those flowers more closely." I no more had the thought when I instantly found myself standing right next to them. They were very tall, about five or seven feet. They were different shades of blue, and the blossoms were beautiful beyond description.

I then looked down at the path that I was on, and I wondered in my mind, "How could this pathway have been built to such precision, so flawless and so smooth?" Again the light seemed to concentrate on the path where I was. Then, like the flower before, it too became transparent, and I could see how it was constructed. Instead of being little round flat stones laid on top of mortar, they were little pillars of stone about an inch and a half around and about six or seven inches high. They were bonded together with some sort of bonding material. As before, when my mind was satisfied, the light withdrew, and I could no longer see into the pathway.

While I was marveling at what I had just seen, I looked toward the sky and saw a very bright ball of light. In the center of the ball, I could see two small pins of light. They were brighter than the light that surrounded them, and I noticed that they were traveling toward me, but were a very long distance away.

As it approached closer, I could see that what had looked like two pins of light were actually two personages in white robes, and they were radiating a light much brighter than the ball of light in which they were traveling. I realized that they were approaching toward me so rapidly that I felt like they were going to crash right into me. However, when they got right up to me, they stopped about four feet in front of me.

They both came forward. One reached out and took me in his arms and held me to his bosom. While he held me, I could feel three distinct feelings. First, I felt a very warm sensation that engulfed my whole body. Second, I felt an overwhelming feeling of love that words cannot describe. Third, a sensation as if I was sandwiched between two giant vibrators, and I felt a great, awesome power surging through my entire body. In my mind,

I wondered, "What is this power I am experiencing?" And in my mind came the answer, "It is the power of the priesthood, which is the greatest power in heaven and on earth."

After he held me for what seemed like a very long time, he stood me on my feet and moved back about four feet. At that time I was allowed to see his face. It was my father. As the other individual came forward I recognized him as my grandfather.

My father had died some ten years before at the age of eighty-eight. At that time his hair was mostly gone, his teeth were gone, and he was stooped and wrinkled. He had had some skin cancer removed from his right cheek that left a star-shaped scar. As I looked at my father, he stood straight, the wrinkles and scar were gone, and he had the appearance of a thirty-year-old man. He smiled at me and had a beautiful set of white teeth. He had a full head of hair that was neither white nor gray, but was about the color of a newborn lamb. He then turned the back of his head to me, and I could see his wavy hair.

Then my father held his hands out in front of me, palms down, and then turned them over with the palms up. I am sure he did this so that I would know for sure that he was, indeed, my father. I knew his hands so well that if he had died in a fire that consumed his whole body, leaving only his hands, I could have identified him by just his hands.

I noticed that he and my grandfather were not dressed like the other people who were there. They were dressed in white robes, and the whiteness of their robes was beyond description. They almost seemed to glow. The sleeves reached to their wrists, and the bottom went clear to their ankles. The collar was very large, and it could be lifted up over the head to form a hood. I noticed that they were both barefooted and that their feet were not on the ground, but they stood about three or four inches above the ground.

I then asked him, "Why are you and Grandpa here?" He answered me by saying, "Who else should come? Everything here is done in the patriarchal order of the priesthood." At this time my father then gave me a sermon on the importance of receiving the priesthood and also honoring it. He told me that because he had honored the priesthood throughout his life, it was his right—and also his father's right—to come to me at this time.

I then asked him where I was, and he answered, "You are in paradise." I then told him that I wanted to stay, but he said that I had to return to earth, as my work there was not completed. He then told me many things that I was not to reveal to anyone. I can only say that it pertained to the members of my family and myself. I asked him a second time if I could stay with him, and again he told me that I could not stay. Again I pleaded with him to stay, saying that if I returned to the earth I would be severely handicapped and would suffer a lifetime of pain and misery. However, he told me to go back and do as I had been instructed, and I would be given the strength to accomplish it.

The one thing that was told to me many times was to love my family, my neighbors, and all of my brothers and sisters here on this earth, regardless of their color or circumstance. This I am trying to do.

When he was through speaking to me, he and my grandfather were again surrounded by the sphere of light and began to leave in the same direction from which they had come. At this point I found myself again in the tunnel and was soon back in the hospital. Later the nurse told me that I had been over twenty-two minutes without a heartbeat.

I had not shared this experience with anyone until one day when my bishop was in the room alone with me. I told him that when I started to enter the tunnel, I had heard a voice call for angels to attend me. He responded and said, "Yes, I know. When I blessed you, I felt inspired to call for them." I told him that I recognized the voice as his.

One day as I lay in my bed, I remember feeling very cold. I was also very weak and experiencing a lot of pain. It was at this time I was thinking to myself, "I don't want to live anymore." While I was having these thoughts, I could hear children singing. They were singing about Jesus, and I remember wondering, "Is it Christmas already? Are these carolers out in the hospital halls?" Then I distinctly heard a young child praying, and he asked our Father in Heaven to "Please bless Brother Chidester that he will get well." When the prayer ended, I suddenly felt warm all over. The pain subsided, and I drifted off to sleep.

Three days later, the primary president from our ward visited me in my room and brought with her about thirty handmade get-well cards that the children in primary had made for me. While she was there, I told her of my experience hearing children's voices singing and the prayer uttered by another child. She asked me when this had happened. I said, "Three days ago." She wistfully looked at me for a long moment, then said, "Three days ago we held a special fast and prayer day for you in the primary."

I am now more convinced than ever of the power of prayer. I not only heard that little one praying for me, but I felt our Heavenly Father answer that prayer and bless me as the little child has asked in my behalf.

I testify to all who read this account of my experiences that I know our Heavenly Father lives, that His Son, Jesus Christ lives, is our Savior, our Redeemer, and that He loves us more than we can ever imagine. I leave you this testimony, God being my witness, in the name of Jesus Christ, amen.

About the Author

Candace Kinser, a former ICU nurse, entered hospice and geriatric care in 1997. She became board certified in hospice and palliative care in 2002, and received her Bachelor of Science degree in Nursing from the University of Utah with the Dean's Award for the Outstanding Baccalaureate Student. Candace completed the University of Utah's Geriatric Nursing Leadership program, and was inducted into Sigma Theta Tau, International Honor Society of Nursing. Previously she attended Rose State College School of Nursing in Midwest City, Oklahoma.

Candace has served as a curriculum reviewer for the Hospice and Palliative Nurses Association and is listed in the "Core Curriculum for the Generalist Hospice and Palliative Nurse," as well as the "Study Guide for the Generalist Hospice and

Palliative Nurse." She has been nominated for listing in Cambridge "Who's Who Among Executive and Professional Women."

Candace's passion for hospice is evident in her series, "Confessions of a Hospice Nurse," published by the Utah Nurses Association. Her popular lectures regarding end-of-life experiences are sought after by varied audiences, ranging from small community and church groups to larger groups at hospitals and universities. She has also been a featured speaker for the Utah Nurses Association, the Utah Hospice and Palliative Care Organization, and the Utah Association of Healthcare Auxiliaries/Volunteers.

Candy and her husband, Bob, reside in American Fork, Utah among their large family of four children and twenty-one grandchildren.

Candy continues to serve in the community as a nurse for Yarrow Hospice & Palliative Care, stating that her association with patients, families, and other caregivers is a highlight in her life.